GREEN GLORY

THE FORESTS OF THE WORLD

Also by Richard St. Barbe Baker

I PLANTED TREES

Mr. St. Barbe Baker, with first-hand knowledge of the subject, has written a most useful guide to the world's forest resources and their importance to men . . . The depletion of forests in a great number of regions of the world, if unchecked, is bound to lead to serious consequences. Forested areas can be placed on a sustained yield basis. GREEN GLORY will make a real contribution to an understanding of this fact, and ultimately of the devastation of the land which results from deforestation.

— Fairfield Osborn, author of "Our Plundered Planet," President of the New York Zoological Society, President of the Conservation Foundation.

For twenty-five years Richard St. Barbe Baker, international conservation expert and one-time adviser to President Franklin Roosevelt, has devoted his life to the study of the world's forest resources. He has observed at first hand the destruction which has been wrought and the brave efforts of conservationists to replenish the world's supply of trees. GREEN GLORY is the result of a lifetime of r e s e a r c h and first-hand observation.

In colorful prose, punctuated with many dramatic photographs, he tells the story of the forests of the world. He takes the reader on a bird's-eye tour of our planet, showing us where

the world, and has served as adviser to observation agencies in Africa, Europe, South America, Canada, and elsewhere. In the '30's he worked with President Roosevelt to develop the Civilian Conservation Corps camps. He is the author of several other books about trees, as well as innumerable articles and pamphlets on forestry.

World's Wonder Trees

GREEN GLORY

THE FOREST OF THE WORLD

by Richard St. Barbe Baker

With a Foreword by Howard Spring

A. A. WYN, INC. NEW YORK
1949

Printed in the United States of America
American Book–Stratford Press, Inc., New York

FOREWORD

M R. RICHARD ST. BARBE BAKER, who knows the
forests of the world as intimately as most of us know the privet
hedges in our own back gardens, and who knows individual
trees like the great redwoods as familiarly as we know our
favorite dogs, has put his unique experience of these matters
into a number of books. If I were asked to say in a sentence
what it is that he seeks to teach us through these books, I
should answer shortly: "All flesh is grass."

This famous saying is too often accepted as meaning only
that the life of man is brief. He "to-day is, and to-morrow is
cast into the oven." But there is more to it that that. Every
moment that he draws breath here below man is dependent
on the grass of the field for his very being. Sir Thomas Browne
knew this and pointed it out in *Religio Medici*: "*All flesh is
grass* is not only metaphorically but literally true; for all those
creatures that we behold are but the herbs of the field digested
into flesh in them, or more remotely carnified in ourselves."
In the fourth chapter of this present book, Mr. Baker puts the
same thought into a few words: "Thus the tree, with the help
of all plant life, controls the food supply and life of man and
of the animal kingdom."

If I had been writing that myself, I should have said: "Thus
the tree, with the help of all plant life, controls the food sup-

5

ply of the animal kingdom, and man will forget at his peril
that he is a member of that kingdom."

A great deal of Mr. Baker's writing in all his books—and
the present book is no exception—has been concerned with
the disasters that follow when man forgets that he is not the
world's master, but one of many tenants. The tenants are
animate and inanimate—or so we choose to call them, though
the animation of a tree is an inescapable thing, and some trees
take on the proportions of majestic personality. But, call them
what we may, the farther we go into the matter the more
deeply we apprehend that men and trees, grass and birds, the
beasts of the field and all living things, are held in a balance
that may not lightly be disturbed. Even that which seems
meanest is a note in what should be a harmony and is too
often a discord; which is the inner meaning of that strange
saying that not even a sparrow shall fall to the ground "without your Father."

Not till this is far more deeply understood than it is today
will man approach that condition of prosperity which he now
all too often imagines can be reached by "gadgets." Fall in
with the ways of Nature and prosper; fall out with them and
disaster is inevitable. Not that "falling in" means acquiescence
with all that Nature wants to do. No farm, for instance, is
"Nature" as it would be if left to its own devices. The point is
that Nature must be coaxed and wooed, not ravished; her ways
of going to work must be understood and sympathized with if
we are to attain the ends which are both ours and hers. And in
the long run there must always be a sense in which man, in
relation to Nature, is both slave and master. But this is too
wide a subject to be gone into here.

We find in this book some truly terrifying pictures of man
flying in the face of Nature, ruthlessly uprooting and burning
the very stuff that holds the world together; and no less terrible pictures of Nature making her implacable reply. Man
strips the forests of China; Nature swirls away in the Yellow
River every year 2,500,000 tons of the soil on which man might
live. Man strips the western prairies to the bone; Nature hands
him a dustbowl. So the folly and the retribution go on, and

have gone on throughout the centuries as civilizations have risen and decayed.

Can the process be stopped? Will man learn to work with Nature, realizing, as Mr. Baker so well puts it, that the bounty of Nature is not his to squander, but is an "entail" for the good of all generations? Well, much has been done; how much this book will tell you; and you will learn here, too, how much our author has himself contributed to the redemptive work, with what energy and knowledge he has ranged the whole world, seeking to stem the tide of destruction. He poses the problem in its forbidding magnitude and reaches the conclusion that only concerted action by every country can repair a situation that has tended for so long to get out of hand. He would for one thing—and this seems to me a splendid idea—turn all the standing armies of the world onto forestry work. Goodness knows, the armies have eaten our green life like locusts; it would be only reasonable if they repaired their own ravages.

Would the nations, which seem so fatally disinclined to collaborate upon anything, collaborate upon this? Could they be persuaded that the life of trees matters? They could, if it were once sufficiently known that men and trees live or die together. Here is a small instance with a large significance. To the north of the Gold Coast, Mr. Baker tells us, the destruction of the forest has let in the desert, which is advancing rapidly. The people are being driven into a narrowing strip of trees. "Here may be witnessed racial suicide on a bigger scale than the world has ever before seen. Knowing the end of the forest to be near, and with little chance of getting food, the chiefs have forbidden marriage, and the women refuse to bear children, for they will not raise sons and daughters for starvation."

When improvidence goes so far that one edition of an American newspaper consumes twenty-four acres of forest, it is not difficult to imagine a too-near time when the plight of those Negroes shall be the plight of millions of mankind. Only knowledge, implementing a rational co-operation with Nature, can avert disaster; and I am not aware of any writer who spreads that knowledge more fruitfully than Mr. St. Barbe Baker.

HOWARD SPRING

GREEN GLORY

When God, all glory, fashioned—
Flashed the first bright light
From Heart of hearts,—impassioned
Life of Life, delight
He knew in Nature's green
That ran the Earth around,
A verdant spirit, clean
And pure upon the ground.
Thus waked the soul of Earth
Into a perfect tree,
And all the forest birth
From it, was come to be.
Onward green glory shone
At peace with rhythmic swing,
As leaf with leaf, upon
The trees did timely spring.
Then as the scale did fall—
O'er burdened with green light,
In summer, over all—
Bare branches came in sight
With gesture to up-hold
The sap-returning scale
Of life, that winter cold
Could never long assail.
And so the flame ran on,
With benediction peace;
Thus quiet beauty shone
Green fire, without cease:
And God saw it was good.
Then fashioned He mankind
Whose seed misunderstood
With self-asserting mind,
The glory of the tree,
And with a ruthless hand
Curtailed fertility
Upon the fruitful land.
The flame of glory waned,
And drought and dreary dearth
Laid waste the woods, and planed
The lovely curves of Earth,
Whose soul was gone from sight.
Then man repented him
And strove to kindle light
Where he had made Earth dim.

. . . .

Man now plants many trees
To glorify their birth,
Since God intended these
Should shine from heart of Earth.

—Written for *Green Glory* by CATHERINE BLAKISTON

ACKNOWLEDGMENTS

To SO MANY people I owe a debt of gratitude for the helpful way in which they have assisted me in my lifelong study of trees and forestry. But for their help I could not have attempted this present work. It was my father who first initiated me into the art of growing trees. When I was a small boy he allowed me to work with him in his nurseries in the village of Westend in Hampshire. It is impossible to make acknowledgments to my many teachers whose words of wisdom guided me in my studies in many lands.

More than a formal acknowledgment is due to the diplomatic representatives of the forty-four nations who for the past few years have been co-operating with me, and who have provided information about the forests of their countries. In the course of my travels I have enjoyed the kindness and hospitality of numerous foresters, who have accompanied me to their forests and have opened their hearts about their particular problems of conservation.

To mention all the books that I have consulted would entail listing most of the works on my shelves, but among those that have been especially helpful are: *The Trees of Great Britain and Ireland,* by John Henry Elwes and Augustin Henry; *Timbers of Commerce* and *Textbook of Wood,* by Herbert Stone, Professor in Wood Technology, Cambridge University; *Plants,* by

Sir Albert Seward, Professor of Botany, Cambridge University—
under both of whom I studied at Cambridge; *Aims and Methods
in the Study of Vegetation,* by A. G. Tansley, F.R.S., and Dr.
T. F. Chipp; *History of Forestry,* by Dr. Fernow, Dean of the
Faculty of Forestry, University of Toronto; *The Land Now
and To-morrow,* by Sir George Stapledon; *Alternative to Death,*
by the Earl of Portsmouth; *The Rape of the Earth,* a masterly
survey of soil erosion by G. V. Jacks and R. O. Whyte; *Humus
—and the Farmer,* by Friend Sykes, the last four being published by Faber and Faber, who have sponsored so many valuable books dealing with the land. To *The Empire Forestry
Handbook 1946* I owe many valuable statistics, and my thanks
are due to Major P. M. Synge for his descriptions in *Borneo
Jungle* (Lindsay Drummond); to V. A. Firsoff for *The Tatra
Mountains* (Lindsay Drummond), and to Dr. George Borodin
for an extract from *Soviet and Tsarist Siberia* (Rich and
Cowan). Other books I have consulted are *The U.S.S.R. A
Geographical Survey,* James S. Gregory and D. W. Shave
(George G. Harrap & Co., Ltd.); *Extinct Plants and Problems
of Evolution,* Dr. D. H. Scott (Macmillan & Co.); *Sagas of the
Evergreens,* Frank H. Lamb (The Bodley Head); *Green Moun-
tains,* Bernard O'Reilly (W. R. Smith and Patterson Pty., Ltd.);
Big Trees, Walter Fry and John R. White (Stanford University
Press); *Earth's Green Mantle,* Professor Sydney Maughan (The
English Universities Press); *The Nation's Forests,* William
Atherton Du Puy (The Macmillan Company); *The Structure
and Life of Forest Trees,* by Dr. Bügen, translated by Thomas
Thomson, M.Sc. (Chapman and Hall Ltd.); *The Poems of
Henry Van Dyke* (Charles Scribner's Sons); and the new edition
of *Chambers's Encyclopaedia.* To Dr. Ovid Butler I am indebted for help from his journal, *American Forests,* and to
many friends and members of the Society of American Foresters and to their *Journal of Forestry.* Grateful acknowledgment is due to Dr. Franz Heske, author of *German Forestry,*
who very kindly accompanied me with a party of forestry
students from Oxford on a tour in Eastern Germany, Austria,
and Czechoslovakia

To many of those mentioned in the bibliography I owe a debt for the contact of personal friendship as well as the written word. The assistance of Mr. Henry G. Finlayson, Executive Secretary of The Men of the Trees, has been invaluable, and I should like to thank Miss Sylvia Kershaw and members of Headquarters Staff, especially Miss Ann Gilbert, for typing and taking down rough drafts, and Miss Naish for preparing a fair copy of the manuscript.

Throughout all I have had the inestimable help and support of my wife.

CONTENTS

13

ILLUSTRATIONS

Photographs by the author except where otherwise indicated

Douglas Fir

GREEN GLORY

THE FORESTS OF THE WORLD

1.

THE RHYTHM OF THE FOREST

A FOREST IS a society of living things, the greatest of which is the tree. In a virgin forest, growth keeps pace with decay: at one place a tree will be reaching maturity, at another declining. As an old tree falls, a gap is made in the canopy, light is let in, and many younger trees race with each other to occupy this new opening. This is happening by slow degrees throughout the forest and so the rhythm of growth is maintained.

It has taken centuries to form the floor of the forest. Up to ninety per cent of mineral soils is derived from rocks by a process that is called weathering, which is carried on by alternate freezing and thawing, contraction and expansion, as a result of cold and heat, the action of water and carbonic acid, and the prying action of roots.

It is possible that a forest of today may be standing on a site which at one time was bare rock. Perhaps some lichens established themselves on a damp level surface of the rock. The weathering action of the elements disintegrated the surface and formed a layer of tiny rock particles. This process was hastened by the chemical secretions of the lichens until these mosses were followed by grasses and in due order by herbs and shrubs, and then one day a wind-borne tree seed lodged there

and began to grow, and thus founded a community of trees.
That was how the forest began. Tiny alpine species they must
have been, but their leaves provided the first litter, and in the
course of further centuries the way was prepared for higher
types of forest. As the treed area developed, precipitation increased; growth was hastened as well as decay, acting and re-
acting upon the future generations of trees. In all this, fungi
and bacteria played their part in producing and modifying
humus and litter. Parent trees scattered their seed, which,
borne by the wind, colonized fresh areas.

Each group of seedlings contended with the others for light
and the suppressed and less fortunate in the race fed the growth
of their victors. The trees which attained their full growth
shared the sky and sunlight with their neighbors for a brief
space after so long a struggle. Practically all trees make their
best growth in full sunlight, but there are those more particularly adapted to survive in partial shade; these may form a
second story, their foliage being more dense than the light-
demanders. All trees are more tolerant of shade when they are
young. It is the crowding of trees in the forest which helps
them in their upward growth and kills off the lower branches,
making the timber free from knots.

There is continual decline as well as growth in the forest.
There is no standing still: as soon as a tree stops growing it
begins to decline. Even before this, decay may have set in
within its heart, and it is set upon by beetles and borers, its
roots are attacked by fungi, its huge body is no longer supported, and a mere gust of wind may bring it to earth. It becomes a home for woodlice and millions of other insects, which
play their part in returning the fallen tree to the earth from
which it sprang.

The forest floor is the name given to the ground beneath
the trees in a forest. The mulch is made up from fallen twigs
and leaves which remain on the ground, where they slowly
decay and form a cover of rich mold or humus. This protective covering forms a most useful purpose: it permits the rain
and snow waters to permeate the soil without making it too

compact, thus allowing the air to penetrate, while at the same time it prevents the washing away of the land and too rapid or excessive evaporation from the surface. The humus also assists the decomposition of the mineral substances in the soil, which in turn provide food for the growing trees. Tree growth is less dependent on the condition of the surface soil than it is upon the depth of the subsoil. It has been shown that trees are not exacting on the quality of soils because they make their own manure and fertilize themselves and even provide a surplus.

Whenever man has sought for land to grow food, he has found it in the forest. The story of colonization is that of clearing the forest to make farms. So long as the farms were kept small and tree-surrounded, fertility was maintained and the trees afforded protection for the crops, modified the temperature in both summer and winter, and provided nesting places for helpful birds, which destroyed harmful insects. Above all, the land was enriched by the humus with its mycorhizal associations—the secret of successful growth.

Once the virgin forest is exploited by man, it is necessary to introduce cultural operations to maintain the highest standard of yield. The resulting thickets of fresh growth must be thinned, the mature timber harvested. This is the art of silviculture.

From the forester's point of view, the most important thing is to fit each species into the most suitable habitat. This calls for a knowledge of the factors of habitat, such as moisture, temperature, light, and soil, and the requirements of each species and the demand that it makes upon Nature. These requirements are discovered in the first instance through nursery practice. Seeds are sown under varying conditions approximating the natural forest where they grow. Whole series are provided, and the results carefully observed and tabulated. It would be simple if in nature trees grew in pure formation, but it has been found by experiment that a combination of species tends to give the best results. Certain nurse trees may be required to assist growth in the early stages, while at later

stages another combination of helpful trees is needed to bring
the main crop to maturity. Whereas light is an important
silvical factor, so also is root competition. The forester is concerned with more than what he sees happening above the
ground, for he has to estimate the condition of root growth.
But it is reasonable for him to presume that where the crown
canopy is denser the root competition will be more severe;
therefore the density of the shade should also be an indication
of the intensity of the root competition.

The beneficial influences of a forest are many. Trees are
forever working for man's good. During the day the ground
under the trees is protected from the sun's rays and is therefore cooler than soil unprotected. As a result of this protection, the forest air is cooler than the air in the open, and, as
air is in constant circulation, this tends to reduce the temperature on hot days. At night trees retard the radiation of heat
from the ground under them. This helps to equalize the temperature. To anyone flying over a forest in the daytime the
upward motion of hot air which has been driven into the
forest from the surrounding plains is quite perceptible, while
at night there is a reverse process which tends to drag the
plane down over any extensive forest area.

This same pull may help to precipitate clouds and increase
rainfall in that neighborhood. Trees may increase horizontal
precipitation, while their leaves retain the moisture, preventing a quick run-off to the ground below. It takes time for the
rainstorm to penetrate the leaves and still longer for it to per-
colate through the humus, and longer yet to find its way
through the root channels to the subsoil, where later it will
form springs, which in turn will feed rivers. Evaporation is retarded first by the covering afforded by the shade of the leaves
and second by the blanket of humus forming the forest floor,
thus keeping the water level high. It is one of the most valuable functions of the forest to provide catchment areas, and so
distribute water for growing crops.

The water capital of the earth may be thought of as consisting of two parts, the fixed capital and the circulating capital.

The first consists not only of the water stored in the earth, but also of that in the atmosphere. The circulating capital is that which is evaporated from water surfaces, from the soil and from vegetation, and which, after having been temporarily held in the atmosphere in the form of clouds, is returned again as rain, dew, or snow. The function of the trees is to filter the water and distribute it, and forest cover directly influences the pattern of this distribution.

We cannot yet clearly follow the intricacies of the circulation of water on the earth, in the earth, in the trees, in the ocean, and in the air, but we do know that man's ignorant interference with the forest and other cover has greatly reduced the earth's fertility and is still doing so. The natural circulation of water is a subject which must have our careful study and deepest consideration.

The very life of man—the food that he eats, the air that he breathes, and the water that he drinks—is bound up with the forest; he is dependent on the forest and its cycle must be maintained. The catastrophes that have occurred, such as the Dust Bowl of the Middle West, the flooding of the Mississippi Valley, the famines of China, the droughts of Australia, and the march of the deserts of Equatorial Africa, have been caused when man has broken this cycle.

We can now understand why forests are the ideal covering for the earth, for they maintain the right soil conditions for plant growth, the litter of leaves, twigs, and branches shed by the trees completely covering the ground. This litter may be only two inches in depth, or it may be a foot or more, but the effect is the same. Its first function is to keep the soil from being washed away, but second only to this in importance is that it retains moisture and rain water, which, instead of running off, seeps slowly into the earth, to come up later in the form of springs. This economy preserves the soil in the necessary condition to fulfill its major purpose of producing plant and food growth.

Above the forest floor there are various strata or layers of tree life. In the forest the crowns of the dominant trees form the uppermost stratum; the next may be formed by trees of lesser height; then come the larger shrubs, and, lower still, herbs and in damp climates mosses. In English woodlands there are usually four strata, but in tropical rain forests there are as many as six distinct layers of tree growth. In the lower and middle zones is a tangled mass of woody lianas which weave their strands from tree to tree, often dragging them to earth and thus making the cover more impenetrable. You will understand then how the earth's surface is protected from the torrential downpours, which, but for this protection, would wash the soil away, leaving rock and sand in their wake.

As a forest officer in Equatorial Africa, I have had an opportunity of studying the rapid deterioration that is taking place in forest types. I have seen the forest climax where superb trees vie with each other in the battle of terrific growth and where the forest has reached perfection. I have seen this same area invaded by nomadic farmers who have cleared away the growth of ages and sacrificed some of the most valuable timber in the world, burning it to make ash in which to grow their yams. I have marched for days along forest trails through what to the casual observer might have appeared to be primeval forest, but upon closer examination I found that the whole of this area was pock-marked with clearings. The rhythm had been broken—never again would that forest attain its former glory.

As I traveled northward from the province of Benin, the forest became more open. I left the tropical-evergreen rain forest and soon began to encounter secondary growth. This country was once farmland cut from the virgin forest and now and again are to be seen tall old trees, remnants of high forest standing out in the open grass. Throughout all this area there is constant change, for the equilibrium of the forest has been upset. Northward the deterioration is seen to be more rapid. Almost without warning a new zone is entered where the grass towers six feet or more—cruel, harsh grass which tears at one's boots and makes going slow and difficult. Here I encountered the first fan palms, a sure sign that I was approaching the desert. As the grass becomes shorter the flat-topped desert thorns appear, and there is evidence of many fires in the charred stems of the dwarfed trees. Soon the degraded grass ceases to be able to support animal life, so the nomads cut the tops of the scrub trees to feed their goats, and thus bring about the final extinction of the savanna forest. It is here that the encroaching desert becomes spectacular. The wind-blown sand often reduces visibility to a few yards; its continual movement is a terrifying thing, for man no longer has the power to control this demon which he has let loose. Here indeed is the final result of broken rhythm. The natural forest has not been allowed to resuscitate and heal the scars inflicted by man. When earth's green covering has been removed, the land becomes inhospitable to man and beast, the rainfall lessens until the clouds steadily pass by, leaving the earth parched and dry. Away to the north of the Gold Coast, in the French sphere of influence, the nomadic farmers for years have been literally driven before the oncoming desert. The moving sands have buried their sparse crops and are racing them into the narrow wedge of forest that remains. Here may be witnessed racial suicide on a bigger scale than the world has ever before seen. Knowing the end of the forest to be near and with little chance of growing food, the chiefs have forbidden marriage, and the women refuse to bear children, for they will not raise sons and daughters for starvation.

2.

COSMORAMA

IF ONE were high up in the stratosphere and could look down without anything to obstruct the view, sufficiently far away to view in perspective the North Polar regions, and if it were summer, one would see the Arctic Sea glistening white and hummocky, the Paleocrystic Sea. The ice is in constant motion. The great land mass forcing itself into view is Greenland, a continent in itself. Between Greenland and Iceland and Spitzbergen, great masses of hummocky ice are forever moving, blocking the waters, piling up and cracking asunder—constant movement in all directions.

Whole pine trees are frozen in the ice. Whence did they come? For no living vegetation is in sight. What forces brought them into this maelstrom of ice? Were they carried across the Pole from the rivers of the Old and New Worlds? Their journeyings may be traced back to the virgin forests from which they were torn.

Beyond the masses of hummocky ice lies a narrow band of open land, which runs at great length and varying widths. This is the open brown tundra, with vast swampy plains which border on the Arctic Ocean. They are the Arctic deserts. Here the cold is intense, and the soil frozen to a great depth, for it thaws on the surface only during the short summer. In the tundra plants do not reach tree height, though a few of the most hardy species survive as low bushes, rising but a few inches above the ground. Where trees are not, in the most unfavorable conditions may be found lichens, mosses, reeds, and brightly flowering bulbs of many colors. Where conditions are less severe, small berry-bearing shrubs and those with catkins may be seen, cranberries too, and tiny willows.

Within the Arctic Circle, beyond the tundra, lies a great dark green mantle stretching on and on, almost unbroken. The transition from tundra to the coniferous forest which lies to the south is very gradual. First single trees appear, then groups in irregular formation, and finally the tundra is dotted with thousands of small forests. These are the evergreen forests of the cone-bearing trees, sometimes known as softwoods, although in fact many of them are quite hard, for, having grown slowly in the cold, such trees are notedly tough. Throughout the whole of this region, growth is restricted by a long cold period; yet the forest itself tends to modify the climate, reducing the speed of winds and raising the temperature. The surface soil is thawed in summer. Protected by the foliage, deep snow, and the forest floor of decaying humus, the earth does not freeze to any great depth even in winter, and so it is possible for deep-rooted trees to grow and flourish.

There is a monotony of uniformity in this great green belt which stretches almost unbroken but for clearings here and there for farms. On it goes from Norway, through Finland, the Russias, and Siberia. Here the forests extend to the south of 56° north, covering the slopes of the Altai and Sayan Mountains, and march in the highland regions of Transbaikalia and the Amur Basin. The chief trees of Western Siberia are fir, cedar, spruce, stone pine, and Siberian larch. The Urami, a mixture of marsh and forest, covers large areas. In Southwestern Siberia, fir and cedar dominate, while birch and aspen cover large areas and may be seen with alder, willow, and mountain ash in thickets. In Eastern Siberia the larch forest extends, and in Transbaikalia are pine forests in the deeper valleys. Over all hangs a gloom unbroken by the notes of songbirds. Only in Southwestern Siberia the birch and aspen vary the scene, while in the more open spaces tall rich grass and ferns, with occasional clumps of juniper, bring welcome relief to the monotony of the dark conifers.

In Manchuria and Korea, new forests take the place of this more cheerful vegetation. Evergreen forest encloses the flanks of the Alps, with detached areas in the lands bordering the Mediterranean. In Western Russia are broad-leaved forests and farther east are the steppes. In part of Asia the southern boundaries fade into deserts and the grasslands of Turkestan, Mongolia, and Manchuria. Around the mighty mountains of Tibet the green of the conifers is present and appears in the Himalayas, though these are but isolated outposts in comparison with the great belt of evergreen which runs ever eastward in Siberia, extending from the Arctic belt.

Across the Bering Sea is a tiny spot of evergreen on the island of Saint Lawrence, a link in the land bridge which once connected Asia with Alaska. Over the mountains and winding through the forests is a road, the new link from the East with this once remote part of the continent. Along the Alaskan Peninsula and within the coast range are the magnificent cedar forests interspersed with Douglas and Sitka. In North America the coniferous belt becomes streaky and is enlivened with birches and maples with their glorious autumn coloring.

Here there are four distinct regions: that of the Rockies, with its tree-clad slopes, lakes, and mountain torrents; the prairies of the Middle West, ground hilly, undulating, or flat, with bluffs of poplar dotted here and there; the Great Lakes region around Lake Superior, with vast forests of spruce and pine—pine covering the Thirty Thousand Islands of the Georgian Bay; finally, the forest region of Quebec, with its front door along the Saint Lawrence, gateway to the East.

To the south lies the trail of forest destruction, but here and there are the remains of what must have been majestic forests and abandoned farms are once again being taken in by the trees, showing that Nature heals her scars. In the State of New York, are the nurseries of Syracuse, which are providing millions of trees for the reclamation of marginal lands. The northern hardwood regions are comprised of maple, beech, and yellow birch, extending through the Carolinas into Florida, with its swamp cedar and pitch pine. A dense green tropic zone connects North America and South America. This is unbroken evergreen tropical forest. Greater variety presents itself through the huge territory of Colombia. The northern zone is hilly and dry, and in summer, or the dry season, many of the great trees are leafless. Here are the great macombos and the bombacopsis, occupying the drier, gravelly areas in the region of plentiful rainfall.

Next comes British Guiana with its green-heart forests. The Amazon and its tributaries drain the greatest tropical forests of the world. The somber sameness of the evergreen bush is brightened by the reflected light of the sun on its glistening leaves. This is a region of mystery, and from the air it all looks alike, dazzlingly lovely, with bright-plumaged birds in the treetops and flowers in profusion.

In the heart of Brazil are broad belts of evergreen, and south lie a thousand miles of equatorial and tropical forests along a coastal belt. The coast of this delectable country is swept by the warm current which bears the name of the country. From the stratosphere, Paraguay and Uruguay would blend imperceptibly into Brazil and the Argentine. The vegetation thins out as the rainfall decreases, and becomes more stunted and diminishes, until in Patagonia trees take on pygmaean forms. One must now cross the pampas to the Pacific Coast to pick up the green belt once more. A mere glance will show the great inroads now being made into the main timber forests of the coastal range.

At the South Pole are great mountains of ice—a vast, inhospitable region with an icecap surrounded by the Antarctic Sea, the only unfrozen land projecting into it being the point of South America. The Continent of Australia presents desert conditions, except for the narrow fringe of subtropical evergreen surrounding the coast. New Zealand is made up of open farmlands and sheep runs where unbroken vistas of native trees

once reigned, but once again the pumice lands of the North
Island are being clad with many exotic species, including the
Monterey pine from California.

There are rich forests in New Guinea, Borneo, the Philippine Islands, Java, and Sumatra. Taken as a whole, the forest
wealth still remains intact in this area and with the introduction of systematic management will make a valuable contribution to the reconstruction of the Far East. Great are the
trees of the Malay Peninsula which vie with each other in
their tropical luxuriance. The Indochina Peninsula presents a
great variety of scene, ranging from tropical forest to subtropical evergreen woodlands. Teak is the dominant species of
Burma, and down the Irrawaddy great rafts of this valuable
species float to the port of Rangoon, while up in the forest
elephants are hauling the huge logs along forest trails and
pushing them into swift-traveling currents which bear them
on their way to the great river. India, with its monsoon forests, has a greater variety of species than any other subtropical
or temperate zone, but the hill cultivators have stripped the
virgin forest from many a mountainside and over vast areas
gully and sheet erosion is catastrophic.

Although China claims nearly 300 million acres of forest,
long utilization has ruined the land around the headwaters of
the Yellow River until it has become the worst-eroded region
in the world. In Japan, with its steep valleys covered with loose
volcanic soils, wherever the vegetation cover is broken on the
slopes, immediate disaster is threatened; but vegetation has
been quickly restored, for the Japanese, with their coniferous
and broad-leaved forests, have learned how to control the
threat of erosion.

Across the Yellow Sea the Yellow River is aptly named, for
it is colored with a yellow subsoil that still pours into it from
the now barren loessial hinterland. For hundreds of miles
along its course the bed of the Yellow River is raised higher
and higher above the surrounding country by the continual
deposition of eroded soil, which has torn down the hillsides
in increasing torrents in the most disastrous floods the world

Canadian Spruce for Airplane Construction

The Rhythm of Growth

Broken Rhythm

The Himalayas near Dharmasala, Kangra Valley, India

Flying over the Chechen Gorge in Kabarda

On the next two pages:
"They Stand with Perfect Poise on a Soft Forest Floor"

India with its Monsoon Forests—looking down on Darjeeling

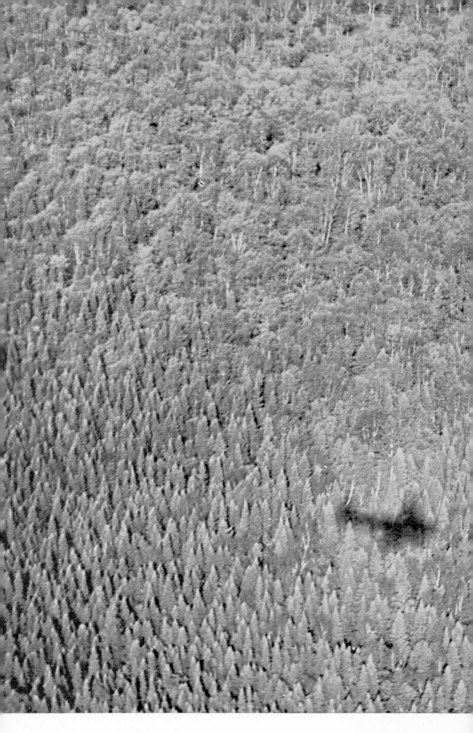

Vast Forests of Spruce and Pine—Great Lakes Region, Northern Ontario

The Forest Happenings of Ages Long Gone—Wood that is 2,000 Years Old and Still intact

Ancient Rhododendron

Old Cypress

The Greatest Tree on Earth

The Tallest Tree on Earth

The Most Famous Giants

Sanctuary of the Woods (California)

Douglas Fir, British Columbia

has seen. Along the trail of ancient migrations and vanished civilizations is little but desolation, untreed desert and the austerity of silence and solitude of the tedious wastes of Gobi and Lob. However breathless the day, a slender spiral of sand is rising. It will move, circle, walk across the plain, leave the earth, and vanish in the sky. At times the whole desert floor is alive with these spirals. To the wanderer in the wilderness they are fearful in their cyclonic force. They are what the travelers call "dust spouts," but the desert dweller calls them "dust demons." Like ghostly beings, they wrap their garments of dust about them and whirl from left to right or right to left —"Male and female," say the men of the desert, "you can distinguish them by the way they fold their cloaks around them, right to left or left to right. See how they come in pairs."

It is hard to realize that the sandy deserts of Turkestan have ever provided pasture for the Astrakhan sheep and camels. Great were the flocks of ancient times in southeastern Karakum, which formerly supplied Bokhara with hides to the value of millions of rubles. Now the advancing dunes, no longer bound by vegetation, threaten the populations in the oases and narrow river valleys, and each year bury large areas of highly fertile, irrigated land. The southernmost point of the Caspian Sea is fringed with evergreen trees and shrubs, while south lie the great plateaus of Iran, once covered with the green glory of the forests. This was the cradle of civilization and as generations grew and flourished, making ever greater demands on the forest land, whole populations passed their prime and became exhausted by the slow wastage that accompanies the processes of natural growth and decay.

The ancient ports of Anatolia are now silted up: Tarsus, visited by Cleopatra's fleet, is now an inland town ten miles from the sea, while the mouth of the Great Menderez River has advanced seawards through upland erosion. Here are countries rich with fruit-bearing trees, for this is the garden of the Mediterranean. The coniferous forest dominates the northern parts of the Balkans, while evergreens emerge in the coastal ranges. Southern Europe is studded with vineyards and citrus groves.

It is hard to imagine that Arabia was once wooded, that Palestine was a land flowing with milk and honey, or that the wilderness of Sinai had manna-bearing trees to feed the old-time wanderers from Egypt. On the continent of Africa little forest remains. Down the East Coast by comparison there is the merest fringe.

In Madagascar, but for the East Coast, little forest growth is present. Along the central equatorial coastal regions of East Africa are the mangrove swamps, extending along a thousand miles of water front. These swamp forests thrive between high and low water, throwing out their aerial roots, which fix them along the muddy creeks. The coastal tropical forest is narrow, mixed evergreen and deciduous, and this borders on the Nika, or desert country, which stretches west for many hundreds of miles. In the mountain regions of Kenya, Kilimanjaro, and the Aberdares are coniferous and broad-leaved zones which fringe the bamboo forests, giant grasses towering sixty feet in height. Beyond the great lakes, there is no forest and sud and papyrus stretch to the north for a thousand miles.

Across the Uganda lie the Congo forests, a stretch second only to the mighty forests of the Amazon, though often regarded as the greatest tropical forest of the world. Not so long ago there were thought to be inexhaustible supplies of many valuable mahoganies here, but these regions of the Southern Provinces of Nigeria and the Congo are honeycombed with native clearings.

The mouth of the Niger in the Gulf of Guinea, with its great inland waterways guarded by endless mangrove swamps along tidal rivers and creeks, is the gateway to the best mahogany forest in the world. Here is evergreen with treetops dazzlingly beautiful, interwoven for the greater part, though broken here and there by clearings for native farms.

Farther north in Africa is the orchard, or fringing bush, later savanna and thorn and tropical grasslands, and, beyond, thousands of miles of desert. The rain forest gives place to the orchard bush and, again, the orchard bush merges into the savannas, which in turn give way to the ever-encroaching desert.

All are progressively deteriorating; there is constant movement as desiccation hastens the march of the desert.

These countries, once covered with thick forests, cradled civilization at its very birth. Here was the very Garden of Eden, where man might have lived on the natural products of the forest without having recourse to nomadic farming; but he bartered his trees for goats and fleshpots of Egypt, forgetting that the earth was the Lord's and the fullness thereof. The earth was indeed good before man fell from his high estate.

3.

FANTASIA

PAUSE IN space and go back in time. Explore the genesis of life on this earth and gain a true perspective. A study of the story of the forests of the past is full of romance. How came they into being? We can but speculate on the mystery of the long journey from the birth of life from organic substance, when by a creative act lifeless matter became endowed with the properties we call life. My old professor in botany, Sir Albert Seward, used to say: "The difference between matter that is dead and matter that is alive cannot be adequately defined. We cannot speak of the one as motionless and inert and the other as endowed with motion and action, for all matter is in constant movement."

The study of the latest teachings of contemporary science leads us to believe that one day in the dim and distant past, when the temperature became favorable, organic life appeared first, in warm stretches of shallow water. Later, as the outer part of the solid earth itself cooled down and became firm, it in turn provided the preconditions for plant and organic life.

From remotest epochs the land has striven against the encroaching seas. There have been cycles in which the land gained in the endless struggle, but such gains may have been small by comparison with land lost, which may be measured in con-

tinents. Those learned in the sciences have produced facts out
of a welter of ancient traditions, and talk with confidence about
cosmic cycles and make deductions for the study of the universe, which throw light on the story of our planet. Geologists
and mathematicians tell us where she is left most deeply scarred
by her conflict with the oceans and where land masses have
been absorbed by the seas. Those of us who are unlearned
in such matters have to accept these scientific deductions, but
there are places in the earth where we can witness for ourselves
instances of struggles between land and water in which the
land was finally victorious.

In the heart of the American continent you can gaze upon a
petrified forest, where the story of the past can be reconstructed
before your very eyes. Here, in a world hemmed in with many
a misty mountain range and long, flat-topped mesas breaking
away in terraces and steps to the plains, where the sun always
shines from the bluest of skies, you can dream of past ages and
interpret their story. Long before the period of cataclysmic
floods, and even before the ancestral type learned to stand in
the posture of man, and long, long before recorded history,
great forests were growing in Arizona, just as in some parts
they grow today. How long ago, nobody knows. Geologists
may relate these petrified trees to the Triassic Age, but who
knows whether they have been there for one million or twenty
million years? Conifers they were—that is evident to botanists
and foresters, who have traced them to the same family to
which the monkey puzzle belongs. Mr. F. H. Knowlton, Bota-
nist of the Smithsonian Institution, has identified them as
Araucarioxylon Arizonicum. Be that as it may, in the course of
time it happened that they were felled, maybe by earthquake,
and there they lay on the floor of the forest when over them
swept the waters of some sea or ocean till their woody tissue
was replaced with silica and became agatized. Millenniums
passed, and then the sea drew back. The plesiosaurus monsters
became extinct; the earth heaved; craters were formed and
belched forth volcanic ash and lava to shroud the story of the
past. But somewhere life remained and seeds found fertile soil

and earth's covering crept back in ever-multiplying forms, only to retreat again before the elemental conflict.

The student of the petrified forests of the vast Northern Arizona Plateau can form some idea of the extent of the epoch-making cataclysms and prodigious events, and gain a perspective which may help him in his study of the world today. Let him remember that the earth, the solid surface of the earth, is forever changing its contour and that it forms waves like the sea, only infinitely more slowly. If the gradual upheavals and depressions of the earth's crust throughout millions of years were projected on a screen in the span of an hour, what a spectacle it would be! Mountains would rise in a few seconds; rocky strata would become fluid, crack, and fall in waves whose crests would tower miles in the air and sink so low that the oceans would flow over them, again rear up so high that the ocean would be drained from them.

We might observe that during the periods of subsidence the incoming waters deposited sand and silt, which in time hardened to rock of many colors, due to the presence of iron oxides. In periods of upheaval the process might be reversed, and the outgoing waters would tear at the mass and constantly strive to bear it away. We can read all this and much more, so let us examine more closely this long-buried forest and try to reconstruct its history from what we can see or read in the geological strata.

Some 10,000 feet of rock was deposited over it and in the course of time eroded clean away. When these ancient logs were uncovered, they were found to be transformed by some magic alchemy, for Nature's chemistry had changed every one into agate and amethyst, into chalcedony and carnelian, into onyx and topaz. Here you can see thousands of acres strewn with trunks and fragments of fossilized wood of all the colors of the rainbow, millions of tons of fragments which, if polished by the lapidary, might embellish the crowns of sovereigns or delight the heart of womankind. Measure these prostrate trees and you will find that some are 200 feet in length and 7 to 10 feet in diameter. One of these huge trunks has been spared by time and spans a canyon 50 feet wide, a bridge of agate and jasper over a tree-fringed pool.

John Muir, who discovered the North Sigillaria Forest in 1906, says that the many finely preserved sigillaria, lepidodendron, and dadozylon trees here, with their peculiar roots and leafmarks, show plainly that in this place flourished one of the noblest forests of the Carboniferous Period, and obviously the trees grew where they now lie instead of drifting in from elsewhere, for there is proof of this in the many standing stumps still visible.

This petrified forest covers many thousands of acres in five separate tracts. In several parts are the ruins of small prehistoric Indian villages, of the Hopi, the Zunan, and other races. Their houses of the Rainbow Forest were as original as they were beautiful, for they were built of petrified logs. Never did prehistoric builders choose more lovely stones for their habitations than the trunks of the trees which flourished ages before man began his long progress on this earth. Hammers, arrowheads, and knives of this wood agate are often found in ruined villages hundreds of miles from the forest.

But search among the fossilized remains of trees that grew fifty million years ago and you will see bones of the dinosaur and other creatures of the prehistoric past. From their fossilized bones and skeletons we see that their organs were developed so that they might attack and destroy each other, but their undeveloped nervous system restricted their evolution and they all, in turn, perished from the earth. Contemporary with them here and in other forest regions of the world, the great conifers were developing in size and stature, purifying the fetid air and in time making it possible for man to breathe.

The birth of protoplasm marked the beginning of the Glacial Period. Only the trained geologist can read the story of past ages as he unlocks his library with pick and shovel. The uninitiated can get little thrill from a fossilized fragment of tree or the humerus of a prehistoric reptile, which are just rocks and stones to him. He has to accept the interpretation of the past that the geologist can give him through his finds.

Paleobotanists—those skilled in identifying tree specimens from rocks or coal measures—place the period at which our forests developed recognizable modern aspects somewhere between the decline of the last dinosaur and the appearance of man. We are told, for instance, that some of the ancestors of the sequoia trees lived from seven to ten million years ago, and that the family was an early offshoot of the *Pinoideae* known as the *Taxodiacae,* including also the bald and Montezuma cypresses and the gingko of Japan.

Those who are skilled in the art of identifying fossilized specimens tell us that there were as many as forty-two different species of sequoias and that they were the dominant tree over much of the temperate and Arctic regions of the world until the beginning of the Glacial Period. But the descent of the ice-cap, sweeping everything before it, was all but the end of that noble line of giant trees. Only two small groups escaped and were left standing in their primeval glory. Small groups by comparison with what had been, and these were in California, where they were protected by the mountain ranges of the High Sierras. There we can today see and touch trees of gigantic size and stature, which provide a living link with geological periods.

The giant sequoias, with their cousins, the coast redwoods, have come down to us as representatives of trees that were abundant millions of years ago, as far back as Miocene times. Contemporary with the now long-vanished dinosaur, suitable vegetable companions for the great reptiles and mammals of the far distant past, they carry with them an atmosphere—unlike the trees of other forests—which cannot be defined in words.

Thus geology is our clue to the study of prehistoric forests. There is evidence that the earliest vegetation on this planet, though of the simplest possible type, was large and lofty. The warm, damp climate would promote luxuriant growth. It is difficult to imagine what the forests of the Archaean Age must have been like. It would take a Walt Disney film gone mad to depict scenes in which gigantic plants and mosses and globular spore cases on long cellular stalks, enormous mushroom growths, and fantastic toadstools of mammoth size reached up into the steamy atmosphere. Throughout all there must have been silent gloom, for no note of songbird, buzz of insect, or rustle of leaf was there to break the endless monotony; none of these yet had being. It may have taken millenniums to evolve the first pines and other primitive trees which formed the vast forests of the so-called Carboniferous Period. It was then that the forests reached their primeval glory. Nothing was more luxuriant or beautiful before, nor has it been since. The evergreen covering reached from pole to pole, for there was no ice or snow. If viewed from the stratosphere in clear atmosphere, our world must have looked like a great green star.

But the atmosphere was still damp and steamy and with an endless haze over all. Even when the sun was high overhead it could not always pierce the gloom of the forest among the aisles of pillared trunks of sigillarias, while towering overhead waved the great branches of the lepidodendrons.

When a storm broke on this forest, the branches would writhe and toss. Mighty trees would be torn from their soft bedding and crash, taking hundreds of trees of lesser growth to earth as they fell. The clearings these made would soon be claimed by younger competitors and vegetative growth, which in their day would dominate that sphere of the forest until other hurricanes came and in turn laid them low.

There were cataclysms upon cataclysms, followed by more millenniums, other epochs, and changed climates, until the close of the glacial periods. Such forests can now be seen at their best only in parts of the tropics, in the High Sierras, and along the Californian Coast.

Such trees as count their age in thousands of years form a living link with the dim and distant past, when man was yet young upon this earth. Walk through the pillared groves of massive trees and you will see their topmost branches pierce the blue of the sky. They stand with perfect poise on a soft forest floor, fern-covered. Ponderous is the strength of trunk

and limb, with almost ethereal foliage. Throughout all, the
light is ever-changing and is reflected in many colors from the
dull, soft bark, while shafts of it are reflected on the mists, and
light the ground foliage. Here, more than anywhere on earth,
we can relive the story of the past and reconstruct the forest
happenings of ages long gone by.

4.

THE WORLD'S WONDER TREES

PIERCING the canopy of the evergreen forest and pointing into the blue of the Californian sky is the tallest tree in the world. There it has stood for at least 2000 years. Surrounded by trees of lesser growth, it has with them survived forest fires, warring Indians, ravages by pests, and depredations by man and beast, while through the centuries it has ever striven upwards in friendly rivalry with its neighbors, understanding the art of living in society and rendering mutual support and protection among its fellows. Storms there have been which have felled less flexile companions and though they have lashed its highest branches, this tree has stood—a miracle of endurance, a pinnacle of beauty, fit to summon forth the deeper feelings of man in wonderment and adoration. Its tender green foliage looked out on the world before the birth of Christ and forms a living link with the history of the past. As one touches its soft bark, contact is made with past millenniums, and one's thought turns instinctively to contemplation of the meaning of life.

It is a fascinating story, 2000 years of growth, with the tree still, as it were, in the prime of life, yielding myriads of fertile seeds and scattering its progeny in profusion. All this time it has shown a rhythm in growth, completing the circle of life.

In the secret of its heart each year it has recorded its history, which one day may be read in its rings.

This tree is just one of millions in a great green belt which sweeps the Pacific Coast from the borders of Oregon to the Golden Gate. It is the dominating species of this primeval forest, which had its beginning when man was young upon the earth; it has witnessed the evolution of man and played its part in producing the life-giving oxygen that he breathes, clearing the fetid swamps where but dinosaurs and prehistoric reptiles held sway. This forest at one time encompassed the Northern Hemisphere and forty-two of its species are recorded in fossilized remains. In other parts of the earth it was destroyed by the icecap, while here it remains as a record of past glory.

The world does not yet know how nearly this green mantle was swept from its last sanctuary. But for the devotion and self-sacrificing ideal of a few friends, these great trees might have followed the fate of their brethren farther south and have been engulfed in logging operations. But after nine years of endeavor, an area of 12,000 acres has been set aside, and there is a still further project of adding to this a Tribute Grove of 5000 acres, a fitting memorial to those who, for an ideal, made the supreme sacrifice.

This coast redwood, *Sequoia sempervirens*, is standing on North Dyerville Flat in the Humboldt State Redwood Park, near several others which closely vie with it. But after searching the world over and comparing my figures of the tallest trees on earth with those of other experts in various countries, I give this noble coast redwood first place for height, for it is 364 feet high and 18 feet in diameter at 4½ feet above the ground.

When I first made its acquaintance in 1932, on a world tour in search of the most interesting trees, it had already been measured by two engineers, who found another tree 361 feet high and 14 feet in diameter at breast height, and yet another, east of the Redwood Highway between Dyerville Bridge and the south end of the Flat, which was 353 feet in height with a diameter of 15 feet breast-high. There was yet another on Bull Creek Flat 347 feet high and 16 feet in diameter, breast-high. Nowhere in the world have I seen so many trees in close proximity which vied with each other in attaining such a dizzy height. How can I convey what this means? Stand this redwood by the Statue of Liberty and it would tower over the flaming torch. Plant it in the deepest part of the North Sea and its highest branches would wave above the water.

In my search for taller trees, I have come across many claims for trees whose pre-eminence in height has competed in vain. I have listened to fabulous figures given me by tree fellers and lumbermen who clamored for the honor of having seen or felled taller trees. Interested as I was to hear stories of pre-existing trees from 400 to 500 feet in height, I could find no living evidence anywhere which would prove that they existed. It might, of course, be argued from existing stumps of great trees that their tops were proportionately higher than any in the world today, but figures show that those greater in girth or diameter are not necessarily greater in height.

The botanical range of *Sequoia sempervirens* extends from a few scattered groups of trees along the Chetco River in Southern Oregon southward in a long, narrow belt to other scattered groups south of Mendocino County, California. The belt is about 1500 miles long, reaching an extreme width of thirty-five miles in Mendocino County, and averaging about eighteen miles. The total extent of the coast redwood area is about two million acres. It occurs from sea level to an altitude of 2500 feet.

This species occupies a temperature range extending from slightly below freezing to a maximum of about 100°. The rainfall varies from 20 to 60 inches. But the most important factor in the growth of the coast redwood is that its range lies almost wholly within the fog belt. The effect of fog in cutting down summer evaporation and reducing soil evaporation is the most important influence in the distribution of these tall trees.

The coast redwoods provide, in fact, the tallest tree from among their ranks, whereas high up on the western slopes of the Sierra Nevada, from the American River on the north to Deer Creek on the south, and between elevations of 4000 to 8000 feet, are the Big Trees—the *greatest* trees on earth.

The highest living big tree in the Calaveras Grove in the Sierra Nevada Mountains was recorded to be 325 feet. Though I have visited the most famous giants, I have not found any much over 300 feet in height. The height of the biggest tree measured was actually 273.9 feet, though it had a base circumference of 102.7 feet. Its greatest base diameter was 37.3 feet, its mean base diameter 32.7 feet, while 8 feet above the ground it measured 27.4 feet. At 100 feet above the ground it was still 18.7 feet in diameter. At about 150 feet from the ground a huge branch came out and went up for 130 feet and where it left the tree its diameter was 7.3 feet. The total weight of this tree is estimated, according to United States National Park Service computation, to be over 12,000,000 pounds or 6167 tons, this weight being divided as follows: trunk 11,- 204,220 pounds; limbs 356,640 pounds; root system 749,760 pounds; bark 15,579 pounds; foliage 9440 pounds; total 12,- 335,639 pounds—and that mighty giant has sprung from a tiny seed half the size of the head of a match. A miracle of growth indeed, which must be a challenge to trees the world over. That tree is known as General Sherman, and it is situated in the Sequoia National Park. The coast redwood is taller and so probably are the eucalyptus and perhaps other trees, but there are none to challenge the bulk of the big trees of the High Sierras.

There are legends of even greater giants, but there is little information concerning heights of pre-existent sequoias. Undoubtedly there have been larger trees than the General Sherman. Just south of General Grant Park, in what is known as the Big Stump Basin, there are several stumps of trees that have been destroyed by fire or by lumbering which are at least 25 feet in diameter several feet above the ground. But these are bare of bark and so must have been considerably larger, for the thickness of bark on the big trees varies from 8 inches to 4 feet. There is one stump in the Calaveras North

Grove which has been used as a dance floor by as many as thirty-two couples at a time. This is thought to be the historical tree discovered by Dowd, a miner of Murphy's Camp, who lost his way when hunting and found himself in the kingdom of the giants.

No other conifer blooms so profusely as the big tree. In late January and February it first flowers, the millions of blossoms at the tips of its fingerlike foliage clustering so thickly that they change the color of the tree. The flowers are heavily laden with golden pollen, and they dust the entire tree when ripe, turning it to gold, while they cover the snow at its feet with golden dust. In May and June the cones begin to form: these are little pearly-gray objects, somewhat smaller than a grain of wheat; but after three weeks they become a brilliant grass-green color, and by the end of the summer they have reached about one third of their full size. Cones do not mature until the close of their second summer, when they throw out myriads of tiny seeds. When fully grown, the cone is from 2 inches to 3¾ inches long, and from 1 inch to 2½ inches thick, and is composed of thirty to forty closely packed scales. At the base of each scale are three to eight seeds embedded in a reddish pigment. The seeds are ⅛ inch in length.

It is obvious that a big tree will bear millions of seeds, but only one in a million reaches maturity. Quality, not quantity, is their motto; only so are they able to develop their gigantic stature and reign supreme in the kingdom of trees. The wonder of it is that seeds from a tree 4000 years old produce as vigorous progeny as those from a mere stripling of 500 or 1000 years. The vitality of the big tree impresses one as much as its size, its majesty, and its color.

Unlike the coast redwood, which can reproduce itself from stool shoots, the big tree reproduces only from seed. But its fertility is low compared with other conifers and the young trees have many enemies. In the virgin forests the most favorable conditions for growth occur only at long intervals, and then only in certain localities. No sooner are the seedlings above ground than destruction and disaster assail them, so

that few survive the first year. Birds, such as sparrows and
finches, are attracted to the tender green plants with the seed
hulls on their tops, and pick off the topmost portions for food.
This invariably kills the plant. Cutworms destroy others, and
large black wood ants levy a heavy toll by cutting off the
plants and dragging them into their nests. Rodents, such as
ground squirrels and chipmunks, destroy large numbers by
eating off the tender tops. Many of the plants take root in
places where the soil is either too wet or too dry, and they
soon perish. So it may be seen that the first year's life of the
big tree is a precarious one, and very few of the many thousand
plants that germinate survive.

Some seeds of the sequoia have found their way to other
countries, where they grow and flourish. In 1854 many were
planted in England, small transplants being distributed by
nurserymen and sold at £5 each. Some of these have already
attained a height of about 150 feet. In New Zealand the big
trees grow much faster than in their native habitat and in time
it is possible that they will outstrip their forebears in the High
Sierras.

Whereas the big tree, *Sequoia gigantia,* is the world's largest
tree, and the coast redwood, *Sequoia sempervirens,* is the
world's tallest tree, the Montezuma cypress, *Taxodium Mu-
cronatum* (*Sabino* in Spanish, or *Ahuehuete* in Aztec), is the
tree with the largest diameter in the world. Arbol de Montezuma, the largest in this grove, is 45 feet in diameter and
200 feet high and was centuries old at the time of conquest.
The grove is located at the base of the rising ground upon
which stands the castle, the ancient seat of the Inca monarchs
and summer residence of most of the Spanish viceroys and
presidents of the Republic. These were protected and cared
for through centuries by the Mexicans, and before them by
the Aztecs, so that they could receive water during their
youth until their roots could penetrate to underground water
supplies, when they could fend for themselves. At the time
of the conquest of Mexico by Cortés, the cypress was much
more widely distributed than today. The extension of agricul-

ture and mining following Spanish occupation resulted in the
destruction of most of the forests. But fortunately, the Span-
iards saved the more outstanding of these grand trees, and, as
with the Californian redwoods, there seems to be no natural
age limit to the Montezuma cypresses. There are over 200
splendid specimens in the park surrounding the Castle of
Chapultepec, two miles southwest of the city of Mexico.

The most remarkable of all Montezuma cypresses grows
in the walled garden of a church in the village of Santa Maria
del Tule, in the Southern Mexican State of Oaxaca, near the
capital city of the same name. El Tule, as the tree is affec-
tionately called, is enormous, and has a base diameter of 47
feet, while above the buttresses it is 41 feet. Its trunk and
crown are unquestionably the largest of any evergreen tree in
the world. It is buttressed at the base, and at about 50 feet
from the ground it branches into huge limbs, forming a
rounded, domed crown. When the sun is at its height it
throws a shadow of 15,000 square feet, equal to a circle of 140
feet in diameter. This tree is 160 feet high. It is impossible
to estimate its age, but there have been many guesses, which
range from 3000 to 10,000 years. All estimates are mostly con-
jectures and the 4000 rings of the sequoias actually counted
by John Muir place them as the authentically oldest trees on
earth.

Other countries vie with the American Continent, for they,
too, have their wonder trees. In the Waipoua Forest, New
Zealand, are the giant kauris, *Araucaria australis,* with their
massive boles which tower without taper for a hundred feet
clear of branches. Smooth as a marble column, the trunks of
kauri are different from those of any other tree on earth. The
largest measured was 17 feet in diameter, containing 214,000
feet board measures with a probable age of 1200 to 1400 years.
The largest recorded tree was 22 feet in diameter, with an age
of 2200 years.

The eucalyptus trees of Australia are greater in height than
the kauris, and may be the second tallest trees in the world.
They provide a greater number of varieties than any other

timber tree, for there are over two hundred and thirty species.

The Douglas fir, *Pseudotsuga douglasii,* of British Columbia, Vancouver Island, and the Pacific Coast southwards, has been described as the world's greatest timber tree, one being measured with a base diameter of 15 feet 4 inches, while the tallest fir, at Ryderwood, Washington, is 324 feet 4 inches; the age of the oldest recorded is 1400 years.

The world's largest pine is the sugar pine, *Pinus lambertiana.* David Douglas reported his discovery of a tree at Umpqua, Oregon, 18 feet 4 inches in diameter, with a total length of 245 feet. The greatest recorded age is 600 years.

The bald cypress, *Taxodium distichum,* has been described as the wood eternal. Its habitat is the South Atlantic and the Gulf coastal region, and it is the largest American tree east of the Rocky Mountains. The one known as the Senator, near Longwood, Florida, has a maximum diameter of 17½ feet, and a mean diameter of 15 feet. Its height is 125 feet, and its age has been guessed at 3000 years.

The world's largest cedar is the Western Red, *Thuja plicata,* and it is to be found on the Hoh River, Washington. It is approximately 20 feet in diameter and 160 feet high, and may be from 800 to 1000 years old.

There are other trees which rival each other in height, form, and beauty. For instance, the world's largest spruce tree attains the height of 230 feet, with a maximum diameter of 14 feet. This is the *Picea sitchensis,* or tideland spruce. There is the Western Juniper, *Juniperus occidentalis,* described as the most beautiful conifer wood. It grows in northern California, with a maximum diameter of 21 feet 6 inches and a height of 80 feet. Its age is probably from 2000 to 3000 years. The Formosa cedar, *Chamaecyparis formosiensis,* is the largest Asiatic conifer, known in its native land as *Benihi.* The Biblical cedar of Lebanon, *Cedrus libani,* the largest of which stands in the Bsharri Grove, Lebanon, is a very old tree. The temple tree of Japan, *Cryptomeria japonica,* holds the honor of providing the world's grandest tree memorial. There is an avenue of forty miles at Mikko, Japan, planted by a poor prince over 300 years ago.

Many wonderful specimens are to be found in the ranks of the broad-leaved trees, such as the sweet or Spanish chestnut, the oak, the beech, the mahogany, the baobab, the camphor trees, while the banyan or sacred fig has been known to cover an extent of 4 acres. It is said that the olive tree never dies, but continues to throw up root shoots long after the trunk of an old tree has decayed. The gingko can trace back its unchanged form through the millions of years, for it was indeed one of the first family of trees.

5.

THE TREE OF LIFE

IT IS WITH awe and reverence that a fellow creature in God's creation attempts to describe one of his elder brethren. In this machine age a tree has been likened to a most delicate machine, but no machine invented by man can compete with the living tree, which runs itself, repairs itself, maintains itself, and recreates itself.

The average person may think of plants and trees as things of beauty and in a vague sort of way realize their usefulness, but little does he understand the complicated workings of that intricate system. We are advised to "Consider the lilies of the field, how they grow; they toil not, neither do they spin"—how much more, then, should we marvel at the growth of a tree.

It is a miracle of growth from seed to maturity. From the kindly darkness of the earth, where germination takes place, the shoot and root progress in opposite directions, the former drawn towards the light, the latter digging into Mother Earth for sustenance. The root explores for moisture, and sends out little branch roots in search of food, which stimulates the upward growth. The shoot in its turn sends out branches, and through the activity of the cambium, or growing layer, the stem thickens. Supplied with a few mineral salts, water, and air, the tree builds up its body, increasing in size as year by year it adds layers of tissue to its growth. The essential chemical processes continue under the influence of sunlight, and, by reason of its unique power of utilizing radiant energy from the sun, the tree obtains carbon for the manufacture of carbohydrates and proteins.

The green leaves which clothe the tree may be likened to the laboratories where carbohydrates and proteins are made, for all the processes of growth take place in them. They build up the framework and add fuel for the maintenance of respiration and the working activities of the whole tree; thus life and growth depend upon the leaves. Delicate indeed is the mechanism of the stomata through which respiration takes place, and there may be hundreds of these minute openings on a single leaf. A hole made by a sharp needle is large in comparison with the size of a stomatal opening. Generally speaking, stomata are open during the day and shut or partially shut during the night. In a single day a birch tree may give off through its leaves in vapor about 15½ gallons of water and on a very hot day as much as 80 gallons may be pumped into the air. It is not only aqueous vapor that passes through the stomata into the external air: the living cells of the tree are constantly giving off carbon dioxide in respiration. On the other hand, it is through the stomata that the leaf receives supplies of oxygen from the outer air; this diffuses into the air spaces between the leaf cells, and is thus available for setting into operation the essential chemical changes by which the energy stored in carbon compounds is liberated and rendered available as a factor in operating the whole tree machinery. But most important of all, and the greatest service of the leaf, in which the stomata take a leading part, is the function of absorbing from the outer air carbon dioxide, which is to be used for the manufacture of sugars. As the carbon dioxide reaches the wet cells within a leaf, it is dissolved in the water which saturates the cell walls, and thence passes in solution through the walls into the living protoplasm containing chloroplasts.

The chloroplasts are well-defined but minute specks of protoplasm which hold in their substance the chlorophyll; this is the substance which gives the green color to leaves. Small as the chloroplasts are, they are able to absorb an amount of light sufficient to enable a tree to manufacture a large bulk of carbon-containing compounds. There are about 400,000 chloroplasts in a square millimeter of a leaf. When we consider that a well-grown elm tree has seven million leaves, and that this represents a surface of 22,834,000 square inches as the total area in a tree, the total chloroplast area in such a tree would be 456,680,000 yards or 94,355 acres or 147.4 square miles. Surely this is an amazing example of mass co-operation. But without this co-operation the tree would not grow. This is the process by which the cells are built up in the tree. It is difficult to form any idea of the speed at which the cells are produced, but if a man were to *count* cells all day and night at 200 a minute, or 105,120,000 in a year, in round numbers he would be able to count 200 million cells in nineteen centuries. Taking the average size of a cell as $\frac{1}{10}$ millimeter, and estimating the number of cells per square millimeter at 100 to 10,000 per square centimeter, he would have counted the cells up to a height of 20 centimeters, that is less than a foot in a single tree of the forest after his strenuous labor extending over 1900 years.

Although we can with comparative ease gauge the chemical contents of the ingredients which go to make up the cells of a tree, their form and quality remain a mystery. How is it, for instance, that the ash takes from the earth and air the elements necessary to form the character and texture of its wood, or the shape of its leaves, or the color of its bark? Other trees growing on the same soil contrive to develop entirely different characteristics. These are mysteries which are yet to be explained.

Another miracle is the manner by which trees cable themselves to the earth and maintain their poise while continually tapping subterranean supplies of water. The roots of a tree serve a double purpose, for while anchoring the tree and providing a mechanical service, they actively take in water, though it is only the younger and more delicate parts of the root system which do this. The actual tip of the root is covered with a protective cap of cells which is constantly worn away as it rubs against solid particles in the soil. With the aid of its *pileorhiza,* it will pass, not merely through crumbling soil, but through stony strata. How is it that so soft a substance can penetrate hard bodies which we break through only by means of a great effort of strength, using tools yet harder? Another mystery, this, how a root without external aid can split obstacles against which man has to employ steel and stone.

The root tips are provided with remarkable osmotic apparatus for the purpose of taking up water and mineral food from the soil. The most imortant source of water for the tree is the moisture found between the solid particles of the soil. This is composed of water particles, some of which can be easily moved, others only with more difficulty. To the former belongs the water which drops from the sample of soil when it is squeezed, while to the latter the water which may still be present even in a comparatively dry soil. The whole sheaf of cells bears the name of *primary root cortex,* and it is destined to serve as the first place of reception for the fluid absorbed by the root hairs. The cortex of the root represents a living reservoir for the liquid taken up by the root hairs, in which larger quantities are accommodated, as well as in the narrow cavities of the epidermal cells. The water channels leading upwards, which draw upon the reservoir, become in this way to a certain extent independent of irregularities to which the activity of the hairs is exposed.

The water, drawn from the depths of the earth, continues to rise by osmotic pressure unchecked through each breathing cell and sieve tube, by way of the growing layer, until it reaches the topmost leaves of the tree. After circulating in the leaves and giving of itself, it absorbs valuable ingredients from the air and returns once more to the depths of the roots, having built up the xylem, or new wood. The xylem is the mass of material to which the cambium gives rise on the side towards the pith in stems, twigs, and roots. At first a cell shed off by the cambium towards the pith hardly begins to differ from its sisters in its growth, but then there also begins a chemical change of its cellulose membrane which is generally finished in the same growing season. This is known as *lignification*. Lignified cell walls are generally more or less strongly thickened and stratified.

The most important seats of life in tree stems are the cambium and the rind. Living constituents extend from there only into the sap wood and their bulk is small compared with that of the dead membranes which form the conducting tissues, and the fibers which serve for the rigidity of the whole structure of the tree. The living cells of the wood act as stores for that part of the food materials, formed in the leaves, which does not find immediate use in the growing points or in the cambium. These materials are collected in the form of starch or fatty oil. These together form a continuous network through the wood, of which one constituent, the wood parenchyma, forms lines running parallel with the boundaries of the annual rings (tangential) and is often only visible under the microscope or a strong lens; while the other—the radially directed medullary rays—is easily seen in many kinds of wood.

In all trees, the bast, or inner bark (the phloem) consists of sieve tubes, which in broad-leaved trees always appear in company with companion cells—bast parenchyma and cambiform cells. These elements together form the soft bast. To the hard bast belong the bast fibers and other sclerenchymatous cells. The medullary rays also, in so far as they extend into the bast, are, in trees, to be assigned to the bast and not to the ground tissue, as they are formed only from cambium cells.

It may be noticed that the fresh green color of the young twig tends to give place to a brown one toward the end of the summer. This change is due to the replacement of the epidermis of the shoot by a periderm which possess the protective properties of the epidermis, but in an enhanced degree. The periderm arises through the cells of the green rind parenchyma immediately adjacent to the epidermis, beginning to divide parallel with the surface of the twig. The daughter cells cut off toward the outside become cork cells, those toward the inside of the twig becoming cells of the green rind parenchyma, and between these two kinds of products there remains a sheath of cells capable of division after the manner of the cambium. This is called "the cork cambium" or "phellogen."

The hardness of a bark or a cork depends upon the form of the cell walls of its elements. If the latter are thin-walled and with large lumina, sponge cork is formed, such as in the English elm, robinia, and spindle trees. The cell walls of such sponge corks sometimes consist in part of cellulose. The cork of *Quercus suber,* the cork oak, and *Quercus occidentalis,* to which we owe sheet cork, belong to this class. The name "stone bark" is given to bark formations which are very hard in consequence of the great thickness of the walls of their elements. Raggedness of the surface of the bark is caused by the stretching of the rind associated with the growth in thickness of the stem of the tree. Theoretically the bulk on the outside of the cambium is as great as that on the inside, but in many species weather conditions cause flakes to come off. The London plane is an example of a tree which sheds its bark each year.

The growing tissues of the tree continue to communicate with the outside world through air passages, the lenticels, in its bark, and through these it breathes. One reason why certain trees will not flourish in cities or industrial areas is that these breathing passages become fouled with the smoke and dirt.

Externally we can watch a tree grow: we see the buds breaking into leaf, shoot, or flower, the branches lengthening and the trunk expanding; but little do we know of the secret life inside the tree. The sudden awakening of the tree in spring suggests that the rising temperature does not find the internal economy of the tree unprepared. It is a fact that what is to be unfolded at the beginning of the next growing season has already been initiated, as in the heart of a seed the form of the mature tree may be seen. In the secrecy of its heart, each tree keeps a record in ring-shaped markings, which may be seen on the surface of the cross section of a felled tree. These marks are the expression of seasonal variations, in the mode of formation of the wood of the tree, which correspond to the change from one vegetation period to another. The elements of

the wood formed at the beginning of the period of growth
activity are of a different character from those which are
formed later and the differences which are present between the
last wood of a period and the first of the following one are in
most species so great that they are evident to the naked eye.
These are popularly known as the annual rings, but there have
been cases in which several rings appear during one year, as,
for instance, in an oak which has been attacked by defoliating
caterpillars. Bared of leaves, growth is retarded as in winter, to
be continued when the new leaves appear.

The tree is man's best friend and one of God's noblest cre-
ations. How dependent we are upon trees has yet to be fully
realized. Only in a vague sort of way can we assess the real
contribution that trees make to human existence on this
planet. Their functions are legion and their life is interwoven
with earth and ether. To the trees we owe the quality of our
food, the quantity of our water, and the purity of the very
air we breathe.

The Psalmist appreciated the balance of Nature and the
place of the tree in relation to the whole:

> He watereth the hills from His chambers: the earth is
> satisfied with the fruit of Thy works. He causeth the grass
> to grow for the cattle, and herb for the service of man: that
> he may bring forth food out of the earth; and wine that
> maketh glad the heart of man, and oil to make his face
> shine, and bread which strengtheneth man's heart. The
> trees of the Lord are full of sap; the cedars of Lebanon,
> which he hath planted; where the birds make their nests:
> as for the stork, the fir-trees are her house. . . . O Lord,
> how manifold are Thy works! in wisdom hast thou made
> them all: the earth is full of Thy riches.

6.

A NEW SAHARA

ALTHOUGH it has taken close on 200 years to create the great Sahara of Africa, it has taken but two centuries to form the Dust Bowl of America. This has been made possible by the invention of the internal combustion engine, modern warfare, and the greed of man.

Three hundred years ago settlers from England arrived on the North American Continent and established themselves at Plymouth and at Jamestown. Around them was nothing but forest. They cut trees to make log cabins and lived on the natural foods of the forest; there were wild fruits and nuts in plenty, and they hunted game. Like the nomadic farmers of Africa, they made clearings with ax and fire for their farms. To these settlers the forest was an enemy to be overcome, and they waged ruthless war upon the trees. From the earliest days of their settlement the home country called upon them for pine and spruce masts for her ships, and for fine oak timber for the hulls of Britain's growing navy. This was the beginning of the lumber industry. For 100 years the white pine of the New England forests was sacrificed to build the houses of the growing colony. This was the beginning of the reckless career of lumbering which exposed the land to erosion and left ruined townships in its wake.

When the white pine of New England was nearly exhausted, the lumbermen waded into the forests of New York, and by 1850 that was the leading lumber-producing state of America. In ten short years those forests in turn became exhausted, for they were cut without any consideration for the future. As soon as the timber was gone, the mills moved on, leaving derelict towns where once had lived prosperous communities. By 1860 Pennsylvania was the foremost state in lumber production and forest destruction. That state, originally known as Sylvania because of its unrivaled virgin forests, and then named after William Penn, was soon exploited.

The lumbermen next invaded the lake states of Michigan, Wisconsin, and Minnesota, where they found dense stands of white pine easy of access and close to water transport. Here indeed was a grand opportunity of exploitation on a scale undreamed of in the previous history of lumbering. Bigger and better mills became the order of the day; thousands of hands were recruited, big towns sprang up like mushrooms in the night, and vast fortunes were made by harvesting the growth of the ages.

It was in the lumber camps of the lake states that the legendary figure of Paul Bunyan arose. He was of French-Canadian origin and crossed over into the United States in "the spring following the winter of the blue snow." Paul Bunyan was reputed to be of such proportions that he used a charred pine tree for a pencil. His inseparable companion and helpmate was Babe, his blue ox, which measured forty-two ax handles and had a plug of tobacco between his horns. So big was Paul Bunyan's shotgun that in an emergency he used its barrels as smoke stacks for his mills. He fought a battle in Upside-Down Mountain with Hels Helson, the Wild Bull of the Woods, and the dust they stirred up settled and formed the Black Hills of South Dakota.

The legendary figure of Paul Bunyan typifies the ruthless exploitation of the forest, showing man's lust for wealth regardless of the next generation.

It looked as though the forests of the lake states were in-

exhaustible, but in sixty years they were as efficiently wiped
out as those of New England, New York, and Pennsylvania.
The mills, starved for the want of timber, were deserted or
dismantled, or moved on with their hordes of workmen. Fires
roared through the masses of dry slash left on the ground, and
even the few parent trees which might have yielded seed for a
new forest were more often than not reduced to ashes. The
sandy land was too poor to farm and bleak desolation ranged
from Detroit to Dakota.

Meanwhile, by 1900, a new lumber boom had started, this
time in the South. In another ten years it had reached its
height. Having depleted these areas of rich pine, the man with
the ax turned to the West, harvested ponderosa pine in the
Rocky Mountain region, cleaned up what he could in Arizona,
Colorado, and Idaho, and entered the last great timber domain
of the Northwest. The giant of destruction, who had accounted for seven-eighths of the virgin forest of the United
States and paid no attention to Nature's laws which govern
regeneration, now made his final assault on the best remaining
timber stand of the world. Washington and Oregon are still
the lumberman's paradise. Here are the Douglas fir, named
after the man who sent the first seeds of these trees to England.
Along a fifty-mile strip between the top of the Cascade Mountains and the Pacific the great trees stand in lordly ranks
awaiting their fate. Many of these fine Douglas fir are 10 feet
in diameter and tower to a height of 300 feet. When these
forests have gone, there will be little left except stands in a
few inaccessible regions. The lumberman will have to retrace
his steps and be content with small trees of secondary growth
which may have sprung up amid the ruins of his making.

For many years, even while all this devastation was taking
place, there were earnest conservationists, supported by the
Society of American Foresters and the American Forestry
Association, who continually strove for legislation which might
check the destruction; but it was only after the Forest Service
was organized that the Government itself developed the idea
of so cutting forests that they would reproduce themselves,

removing only the ripe timber, that woodlands might have time to regenerate. It was Theodore Roosevelt who made the first move by sending Gifford Pinchot to India to study the question for the Department of Forests. On his return, Pinchot brought into being the Forestry Service under the Department of Agriculture, and for the first time an attempt was made to regulate felling and apply more conservative methods.

While the lumber magnates were turning the virgin forests into dollars, the farmers of the Middle West were growing wheat to satisfy the needs of the population which had sprung up on the wealth of the woods. The Industrial Revolution in England gave rise to a demand for cheap food and this led to further plowing of the prairies of the Middle West. Never before in the history of the world had wheat been produced with so little labor; crop after crop was extracted from the deep rich loam of those farmlands, until the soil became exhausted, and was then abandoned for fresh virgin lands to the west. Here was a repetition of the nomadic farmers of Africa, only this time it was on a gigantic scale. Instead of the man with the machete, it was the man with a plowing outfit: first with his gang plow and six horses, breaking 4½ acres of virgin prairie each day, then with a tractor enormously increasing his speed in exploitation—but always leaving derelict land behind him. It was a rake's progress which spelled inevitable ruin.

Such exploitation of the soil deprives it of its protective covering. The land was denuded of trees, scorched by burning, exhausted by overgrazing of the herbage, deprived of its humus by constant cropping without replenishment and inevitable disaster followed, and the beginnings of a new Sahara were laid. During the dry season the ground surface was reduced to dust and swept along by the wind. Without forest protection, these winds gathered force and played havoc with the denuded lands. When the rain came it was of little value, for the dust could not absorb it, and what remained of the soil with its valuable salts was washed along the gullies to the flooding rivers. It has been estimated that since America was settled an area equal to the total area of cultivated land in Germany has been denuded of its surface soil. At the time of World War I wheat fetched peak prices, and every available acre of land, whether suitable or not, was plowed for grain. After the war, when prices dropped, whole farmlands were abandoned, and, being uncultivated, were at the mercy of the elements. Standing one day in Chicago I was choking with dust and upon asking my companion the cause of this unpleasant experience received the reply: "Oh, that's the Dakotas." This dust was what remained of the topsoil of once rich wheatlands and was blown by the wind for hundreds of miles, not only causing discomfort in the cities to the East, but baring the rocks from which it came.

Eminent authorities in the United States have given ominous warnings. A distinguished American engineer some twelve years ago said that with continuance of the manner in which the soil, the mainstay of individual and collective life, is now being squandered, America has left to it less than 100 years of virile national existence. And, if that represents a reasonably accurate statement, it is vastly more significant—if the nation is to win against the accelerated progression of this gangrenous growth of soil erosion—that there are probably less than twenty years in which to build up techniques, to recruit fighting personnel, and, most difficult of all, to change the attitude of millions of people who hold that ownership of land entails the right to maltreat and even to destroy it, regardless of the effect on humanity. This solemn warning was reiterated in 1946 by another American authority, who pointed out that one-eighth of the crop land of the United States has been ruined by erosion, another eighth nearly ruined, a further quarter has lost more than half its topsoil, and that on a further quarter erosion is already under way. This same authority has predicted that a hundred years from now the United States will not be able to sustain a living man.

This is a drastic statement and there is evidence that the warnings are being heeded. As far back as 1926 I had the privilege of meeting, among my fellow delegates at the first

World Forestry Congress in Rome, representative foresters from the United States who invited me to visit their country with a view to assisting them to initiate a more progressive and extensive program of conservation and reforestation. This I was pleased to do, and at the invitation of Gifford Pinchot I met two hundred members of the Society of American Foresters in Washington, D.C. I was granted an audience by President Hoover, who, although at that time he did not see his way clear actively to participate in the cause I had at heart, gave me introductions to the heads of departments. I then set out on a nationwide tour, and, for the better part of two years, devoted myself to preparing a plan. This gave me an opportunity of making a close study of the forestry situation from coast to coast. In every case I had the great advantage of valuable help from foresters, park superintendents, and officials, and was thus able to form a general appraisal.

It was evident that the situation called for immediate action, the rate of timber consumption, including loss by fire and other destructive agencies, being four times as great as the rate of timber growth. The country's requirements amounted to about 25 billion cubic feet each year, while but approximately 6 billion cubic feet was being grown. I recalled that in 1909 the United States produced its entire newsprint supply, but at the time of my survey I found that the country was dependent upon foreign resources for at least two-thirds of it. One Sunday edition of a metropolitan newspaper was using 24 acres of forest a day, while a Chicago paper required 100 acres of Canadian forest every week. The United States, already Canada's biggest customer, was being driven back on Russia for supplies. I saw shipments coming from Archangel in the Baltic up the Saint Lawrence and being transshipped for Erie, Pennsylvania. To me it seemed a tragedy that this great country should be driven back on Russia for supplies; this country which was already using more wood per head of population than any other country in the world.

During 1932 I traveled 17,000 miles throughout the forest areas of the United States and visited cut-over areas and wit-

General Grant Tree

Small Trees of Secondary Growth Spring Up Amid the Ruins—Sand Encroaching on Sitka Spruce in Clatsop County, Oregon

One Sunday Edition

Plowing under Green Manure

The Ground Prepared

Left: A Russian Birch Wood

Below: Timber Being Floated Down the River Pruth in the Carpathians

On the next two pages: Laguna Sand Dunes Slowly Burying a Cedar Forest

Burned-over Area after Logging, Oregon

All That Is Left of a Once Happy Forest Home

Alder and Willow Brush Being Blanketed by Heavy
Sand Encroachment

Gully Scalped and Planted

The Same Gully after Five Years

In Switzerland the Forests are Regarded as Most Important—
Lauterbrunnen, Where the Trees Prevent Avalanches

The Finished Shelter Belt

A 20-Acre Field Completely Enclosed by Windbreaks (Nebraska)

Terraced-strip Cultivation, with Terrace Orchards in Contour and Windbreaks

One-year-old Trees

The Same Trees at Six Years Old

Green Gold of the North—A Norwegian Spruce Forest in Winter

Aerial View of Contour-planted Orchard

nessed the destruction caused by forest fires. I saw the dreaded scourge, hurricane-driven, death-dealing flames; at times I fought forest fires alongside of foresters, and heard many stories of the destruction of human life and property. It was a fact that the United States was losing by fire every year enough wood to build five-room houses for the entire population of a town of 500,000 inhabitants. In California alone 1½ million acres had been burned over. Some years before I was there, one fire in the San Bernardino mountains burned over an area of 15,000 acres and destroyed 3 million feet of timber—yellow pine, sugar pine, cedar, and fir. Before that, in the North-western Minnesota fire, 400 people were burned to death, 2000 were more or less seriously burned, 13,000 were rendered home-less, and 26 towns and villages were partially or completely destroyed. The area covered was 2000 square miles.

While camping with an old Indian in the redwoods in Northern California, where I had been in search of the finest groves, many of them being threatened by the ax, suddenly over the campfire one night, almost out of the blue, the old Indian remarked, "Plenty men no get work; there'll be plenty forest fires this summer." He was a man of few words; in fact, for the previous three weeks we had spoken little, most of our intercourse being carried on by signs. This remark therefore caused me to think very deeply. Under the existing régime in those days men were employed at the rate of five dollars a day to put out forest fires, casual gangs were taken on, and no sooner was one fire under control than another would spring up, so that such men would have almost continual employment throughout the summer months. Did the old Indian mean to imply that persons needing employment would set fires going to keep the gangs employed? I remembered that in Canada I had been told that the Forestry Department had abolished payment for casual fire fighters and had thereby reduced forest fires by over fifty per cent.

From California I went up through Oregon and Washington and saw the last great forests in these states being exploited. From Washington I crossed the Canadian border into British

Columbia, and was distressed to learn from the foresters that they were nearing the end of the virgin Douglas timber. I crossed the Rockies and went up into the Peace River district, where I camped with a Canadian Indian, and after some weeks of careful planning and preparation I set out to find the man who could bring order out of chaos.

Coming from the last fertile country of the West, I met hundreds of distracted farmers from the United States. They had come from the newly formed Dust Bowl. Many of their farms had been buried by drifting sand, or the topsoil had blown away, making it impossible for them to grow any sort of crop. They had heard of the deep, rich black loam of Northwestern Alberta, and were moving north to continue their nefarious work of wheat growing and ultimate destruction. They told me that in many of the worst-hit states nearly all the farmers were getting out. After perhaps three successive crop failures, the farmers could not stand it any longer. I listened to their bitter humor, knowing they were unconscious that they themselves had wrought the destruction and were fleeing from a hell of their own making.

Such meetings and conversations made me feel that my task was all the more imperative and I pressed on across the continent back to the East. Everybody was discussing the pending presidential election. In New York I met two young friends who were great admirers of Norman Thomas, the Socialist candidate for the presidency. Mrs. Norman Thomas ran a restaurant near Gramercy Park, and there we lunched. After an excellent meal, I drove my young friends down to the Thomases' home on Long Island, where I briefly discussed my plan with Norman Thomas himself. Almost immediately he said, "Roosevelt is your man; he is going to be the next President. Come and have a swim!" The three of us accompanied him to his swimming club, and that evening I wired Franklin D. Roosevelt for an appointment.

Driving up through the night from New York, I arrived in Albany about six the next morning, and just before ten o'clock I was awaiting my appointment at the Capitol. I was

greeted warmly by Franklin D. Roosevelt, who exclaimed, "I
have been wanting to meet you for a long time." And I replied,
"Me, too, you. Do tell me how was it you first became interested in forestry?" "I was staying in your country," he said,
"back in 1905, with the Novars in Scotland—Lord Novar was
Sir Ronald Munro-Ferguson in those days, and my wife is a
kinsman of his. He took me round his woodlands, 20,000 acres,
and showed me how he had been able to stem years of agricultural depression by falling back on his woods. He was able to
give employment to his dependents in his forests when there
was no work for them on the farms." F. D. R. told me that
when he got back to New York he sought out Gifford Pinchot,
who pulled out of his pocket two pictures: one was of a painting made in China 300 years ago, and the other was a photograph taken of the same site that very year. In the first the hills
were completely covered with an evergreen forest. At the base
of the hill there was a populous city, settled in a fertile valley
with a river running through it. The only indication of logging to be seen in the painting was a little water chute with
some logs coming down the slipway. The photograph taken
300 years later showed the same contour of the hills, but they
were bleak and bare. Not a vestige of their former glory remained. The one-time fertile valley was strewn with great
boulders, the cover gone, and the dried-up soil with its fertility lost forever. All that remained of that flourishing city was
a few derelict huts. Mr. Roosevelt said that that had made
such an impression on him that he asked Gifford Pinchot to
come and talk to the businessmen of New York. Mr. Roosevelt
said, "From that time I have never looked back. You know
what I have done by way of planting on my own place at
Hyde Park, and you know what I have done for the State
of New York." I said, "Yes, indeed. I know that here you have
planted sixty per cent of all the trees planted this year in the
whole of the States and now you are going to do for the whole
country what you have done in the State of New York." He
looked straight at me and said, "What do you mean?" I replied, "But you are going to be the next President." "What

makes you think that?" he retorted. "Well," said I, "I have just done 17,000 miles in your country, preparing a forestry plan, and don't you think an outsider often has a better perspective than the man on the spot? Besides, yesterday I was discussing my plan with Norman Thomas, and he said, 'Roosevelt is your man; he's going to be next President.'" "Did he say that?" "Yes, he believes you will be able to bring relief to millions of unemployed as he would like to have done if he had a ghost of a chance of the presidency. Do you know you can give immediate and direct employment to 250,000 young men in forestry?" And his quick reply was: "Couldn't you make it 300,000?" I told him how I had just been visiting my old University of Saskatchewan and inspecting the agricultural station at Southerland, where ever since my student days they had been experimenting with the most suitable trees for shelter belts, and how I wished that every farmer, instead of planting a wind belt around his home, would plant a belt of trees around his farm. We discussed the truly alarming problem of unemployment: there were already 18 million unemployed, and it appeared that the figures were mounting by mathematical progression; it had been calculated that before long there would be over 30 million workless and penniless in the United States. I told him of my sojourn in the redwoods and what the old Indian had said about unemployment and forest fires and how in Canada as soon as they stopped paying casual labor for fire fighting they reduced forest fires by fifty per cent. At that moment, like a flash, Mr. Roosevelt caught the idea which later brought the Civilian Conservation Corps into being.

7.

RECLAMATION

WHEN Franklin D. Roosevelt became President of the United States in March, 1933, he assumed office with the country apparently heading for disaster. The theme of his acceptance speech in Chicago was "Back to the land with forestry—without vision a people perish."

On my return to England after the Ottawa Conference, where I had read a paper on the world forestry situation, I busied myself with the preparation of plans for employing some thousands from the distressed areas of Britain, but failed to find another Roosevelt. On hearing the result of the presidential election, I cabled my congratulations to F. D. R., and by return post I received a charming letter from him from Warm Springs, which prompted me to take the next boat out. On my arrival, I conferred with Henry Morgenthau, Jr. I met him in New York. At that time he was Chairman of the Farms Board of that state and he was Governor Roosevelt's right-hand man in the valuable task of bringing the marginal lands back within the scope of forestry. These areas once had borne pine forests, and after the trees had been swept away attempts had been made to farm, but with very disappointing results. Considerable success had been achieved by Mr. Roosevelt and Mr. Morgenthau, with the result that out of 100,000 acres of planting throughout America during that year, 60,000 acres had been planted in the State of New York.

While I was with Henry Morgenthau I recalled briefly my audience with the President in Albany, and said: "What you and the President have done for the State of New York you can do for the whole country. You can plant trees and grow gold for the nation and by so doing can serve the land, assist agriculture, and help to stem the oncoming timber famine." I pointed out that it was on the strength of my report that the largest reforestation corporation in the world had been launched. I presented him with figures which he immediately questioned, raising objections on many accounts, although I instinctively felt that he was already on my side, but wanted to be further convinced and equipped for the great task which was awaiting him. In this thinking, hard-headed man of affairs I felt the emotion of the ideal, and, although his head was in the clouds of altruism with the thought that the plan before him was going to bring fresh hope to many thousands of unemployed, yet his feet were on a very solid foundation—the earth of economics. I had to prove to him the economic aspect of the project which I laid before him. His masterly mind was forever turning my vision of growing trees into financial returns, and where I thought in millions of acres, he thought and spoke in billions of dollars. Quickly he gasped the significance of my figures—figures laboriously collected over many years of practical experience in many lands. He swiftly absorbed them and, instead of crabbing the scheme, wanted to make it even bigger.

He had been a patient listener, but he could also be a most convincing talker. When he had absorbed the project, in his mind the idea quickly evolved into a nationwide scheme. The child of my idea had grown into a giant before my very eyes. Working in close collaboration with Morgenthau, President Roosevelt requested $3,000,000,000 for work relief as his first measure when he was installed at the White House. The second measure was to establish the Civilian Conservation Corps.

On March 22, 1933, Robert Fechner received a long-distance call from the White House requesting his immediate presence in Washington. That very evening a bill had been sent to Congress by the President proposing the setting up of a vast army as a measure partially to relieve unemployment and, at the same time, to accomplish useful work. Congress enacted the legislation and the President signed the bill on March 31. On April 5 Robert Fechner was appointed Director of the Civilian Conservation Corps. The next day the President sent for him and asked him how long it would take to get the first conservation camp going. The director thought it would take some time, but the President said, "I want the first camp going in three weeks' time." And it was.

I was glad to be able to spend the first few months of this great President's term of office in the United States, where I was able to watch and confer with those who were responsible for bringing the new camps into being. I saw the young men in action and joined them over the campfires at night, when I would tell them of my own experiences as a forester. I also gave many broadcast talks in support of conservation.

The creation of the Civilian Conservation Corps was a stupendous task, but the genius of the President inspired the co-operation of the four departments—War, Interior, Agriculture, and Labor—whose united efforts achieved unprecedented success. Under the competent supervision of trained foresters and technicians of Federal and State departments and agencies dealing with conservation matters, some 250,000 young men, with a sprinkling of more experienced war veterans, were soon forming camps and carrying out valuable work. These lads were before long planting new forests with the little trees of their raising, strengthening forest and park protection systems to reduce forest devastation by fires, insects, and disease, and thinning cut-over areas to make woodlands more productive. By the second year there were 300,000 men working in the Civilian Conservation Corps, and by the fifth year there were 4,500 camps, of 200 men each, operating in state and private forests. As many as 300,000 men a day would set out from their camps to plant trees, build trails, erect fire-protection towers, lay telephone lines, and improve grazing conditions in national forests and in public domains. On the deserted farmlands they were able to carry out valuable work of reclamation and rehabilitation. They drained ditches, built check dams, and planted quick-growing trees and vegetation to protect farmlands from soil wastage, to conserve water, and to prevent floods. They conducted campaigns against the deadly white-pine blister rust, the gipsy moth, bark beetles, and rodents. They improved conditions for wildlife and did a host of other jobs related to the national task of conserving and rebuilding America's natural resources.

Those who have not experienced life in the wilds have little idea of the hardships endured by these new recruits. Floods and forest fires exact their toll of human life. Even in the ordinary activities of everyday work there are frequent opportunities calling for quick decisions that may save a pal from injury or death. In fighting forest fires, the young men of the CCC performed a service of the highest order. Several hundreds of these gallant lads will never forget their terrible experience in the Blackwater Canyon, where the worst fire for over a quarter of a century took toll of one human life with every 1000 acres of timber destroyed. The most spectacular work accomplished by the CCC was in this field of forest-fire prevention. Before they had been operating very long, they reduced forest fires by seventy-five per cent. They cut thousands of miles of trails for the purpose of fire control; they cleaned up cut- and burned-over areas and thus reduced the fire risk. Hundreds of lookout towers were built, and manned by trained observers. They prepared proper camping sites for tourists who followed their trails, and, by building stone fire hearths, greatly reduced the risk of a forest fire through carelessness.

Next in importance comes land reclamation, before soil-erosion-prevention operations have been completed on a nationwide scale. It was a noble conception of the President to plant a wall of millions of trees down the center of the United

States, consisting of windbreaks extending 1000 miles, from the Canadian border down to the Panhandle of Texas. The wall consisted of a series of belts, 100 miles wide, comprised of drought-resisting species. This backbone of trees was intended to check the wind which for years had carried away the soil of the farmlands, and also to serve as a trap for moisture. The trees planted were suited to the climate, and the shrubs on the outside rows acted as windbreaks. Even among the experts there were many who prophesied failure; but, in spite of adverse conditions, the entire appearance of the countryside is now being changed. Little trees that were planted in shifting sands in 1934 have attained a height of 40 or 50 feet. The shelter-belt strips have transformed the sandy desert and have broken the flat monotony of the plains. Helpful birds are once more returning and the farmers are again able to plant under the protection of the sheltering trees.

Not all trees will grow on the prairie, with its low rainfall, severe winter, and hot summer. It has been the task of foresters through long years of research and experiment to determine which trees and shrubs are best fitted for the ceaseless battle with the prairie winds and droughts. Among the trees which were found to be best suited for shelter-belt planting in the Great Plains area are the cottonwood poplar, green ash, Chinese elm, bur oak, hackberry, honey locust, and, less extensively, willows. Shrubs chiefly used include lilac, wild plum, and Russian olive. In the Dakotas and Nebraska, the principal shrub used is the caragana, with some chokecherry. Farther south, from Nebraska to Texas, the black locust (or false acacia) has been found an excellent tree for shelter belts and is widely used. This is one of the best trees for increasing the fertility of the soil; it is leguminous and injects nitrogen into the earth. Phenomenal crops have been grown near its roots. Other valuable trees used in the South are the apricot, black walnut, catalpa or Indian bean, Russian mulberry, osage-orange, and pecan nut. The desert willow has been found a satisfactory shrub in Oklahoma and Texas.

From the nurseries of the Prairie States Forestry Project

come the trees for the great planting program. The majority of these nurseries are leased from local professional nurserymen.

The foresters make a point of collecting as much seed as they can locally, for it has been found by experience that seed from a distance does not produce trees fit to cope with the severe conditions with which the young trees have to contend.

Here and there are pioneers possessed of initiative and vision who have set the example which others now may follow. One of the most outstanding of these is J. J. Lydick, of Craig, Nebraska, who nearly thirty years ago started planting shelter belts on his farm of 240 acres. It was two miles from the loess hills, which with the bluffs and flats extend twenty miles from the Missouri River. It was open land, devoid of trees. The average annual precipitation was 28 inches, though at times it was as low as 15. The water table was over 60 feet below the surface. It was a land of wind and dust, with wide extremes of temperature.

The story of his planting has been told by M. B. Jenkins in *American Forests,* the journal of the American Forestry Association. He tells how, soon after Lydick started to farm, hay fever so reduced his vitality that his doctor said he must go to the mountains, where he could breathe the scent of the pine, spruce, and fir and thus escape the dust-laden atmosphere of the plains. But this young man was in love with farming and was loath to leave his land. He decided that, if it was the scent of the pines and the spruce and the fir that he needed, he would plant them there on his own place. He started collecting seed and raising young trees in nursery beds. He chose Colorado spruce, Douglas fir, Austrian and ponderosa pine, and Norway poplar, and he arranged them with slower-growing trees on the outside and evergreens forming an impenetrable barrier against wind and storm. He transplanted them two or three times in nursery lines, so that they might become well rooted before being planted out into their final stations. He took pains to cultivate the ground within the belt that he planted. However busy he was, he always gave the trees his first attention. His neighbors ridiculed him for his pains and for wasting so much valuable land growing trees. "It will never pay," they told him, and yet today, thirty years afterwards, there are many of his old neighbors who would like to exchange farms with him.

Lydick proved that permanent, well-arranged farm plantings and crop shelter belts are as much of an asset as barns or plows. They are as essential to agriculture as modern factories are to industry. The hardiness and present vigor of the trees on that Nebraska farm speak well for the wise selection of seed and the choice of species. Even during the drought years of 1934 and 1936, not a single conifer was lost, although the precipitation fell to 15 inches. Within the zone of protection from these living green walls, the average farm crops were more than double those which grow on the outside. In the drought year of 1934, potatoes yielded 200 bushels to the acre, while other potato fields in the same county dried out. That year not a single bushel of potatoes was grown within a radius of ten miles of that tree-surrounded farm. The cornfields were not irrigated, but the yield was from 35 to 40 bushels to the acre, while neighboring fields without the benefit of the shelter belts were burned up by hot winds. The orchards were an inspiring sight. Apple trees were loaded to breaking point with fruit of good size and quality and close by were large patches of heavy-yielding raspberries.

When Mr. Lydick was asked how he accounted for such heavy yields, he said that he attributed it to the fact that the winter snows melted where they fell instead of being driven into drifts miles away, as is often the case. The protection provided by the trees reduced the force of summer winds, so that they caused little loss of soil moisture; nor had they carried away the valuable light humus particles of the upper soil. This pioneer had found that he did not need much rain to grow crops so long as he kept the soil light and friable. It is interesting to note that Mr. Lydick never irrigated his trees, but depended entirely on cultivation, and this only for the first three or four years. Yet he has produced specimen trees and symmetrical windbreaks such as cannot be equaled anywhere

else in Nebraska or the United States. This planter of trees
has rendered a valuable service by demonstrating how shelter
belts conserve soil moisture and increase the productiveness of
the land. What is more, after thirty years he has completely
regained his health and now lives to enjoy the fruits of his
labor.

Such work is an example of farm forestry such as was advocated by Nebraska's apostle of planting, J. Stirling Morton,
the author and founder of Arbor Day, who continually urged
settlers to plant a portion of their grasslands to trees. He assured them the trees would control wind and water erosion,
afford comfort and better living conditions, and provide future
wood supplies. He foresaw the time when the roads and high-
ways from the Missouri River to the Rocky Mountains would
be lined with coniferous and hardwood trees.

It was through the influence of J. Stirling Morton that the
American Forestry Association, at a meeting in Omaha, Nebraska, in September, 1898, passed the following resolution:

> Whereas this Association believes a proper series of
> wind-breaks would so regulate the surface air currents as
> materially to reduce evaporation, thereby conserving a
> precipitation that under those conditions would be ample
> for grain husbandry; THEREFORE BE IT RESOLVED BY THIS
> ASSOCIATION that our National Congress should create a
> commission for the purpose of investigating the feasibility
> of establishing forest wind-breaks on the plains of New
> Mexico, Texas, Colorado, Kansas, Wyoming, Nebraska,
> and the two Dakotas.

It would appear that no action was taken at the time, but
this is a historic document which is significant of the plans and
purposes of a forward-looking group of forestry pioneers. Although much planting was done by some individual farmers,
many failed, for they had not arrived at the knowledge of the
best technique. Tree survival depends on choice of species,
source of seed, and the provision of adequate cultivation dur-

ing the early years of planting. Wherever farmers have succeeded with their trees they have generally become successful
with their farm crops. The combined experience of the pioneer planters indicates that farm forestry is an important factor
in the solution of food production and ultimate human survival.

The American people have now accepted this reclamation
by tree planting as a vital part of their future program. The
foresters working on this project picture an environment where
man and beast will obtain cover from the fury of the elements.
The launching of the CCC inaugurated a nationwide war of
reconstruction—not a war of destruction. It was waged to build
up America's human and natural resources. That struggle was
fought on two fronts. On the one hand, President Roosevelt,
through the CCC camps, was able to save an army of idle
youth from the moral erosion caused by unemployment, while,
on the other, he attempted to save his land from deterioration
and barrenness. The President appealed to their imagination.
Were they not the sons and the grandsons of Americans who
had conquered the West, always moving that frontier farther
and farther back? By launching the CCC, he created a new
frontier for them, and hundreds of thousands of these young
men, who would otherwise have had little or nothing to do,
were sent to outdoor camps in the forests and parks, where
they were given jobs—re-creative jobs in the fullest sense of
the word. They were taught self-discipline, not military training. This army in turn co-operated with Nature in helping to
restore the green glory to the hills and fertility to the valleys
and plains.

8.

THE BALANCE OF NATURE

EARTH'S green covering is the basis of life, whether human or animal. Vegetation constitutes the foundation of our energy and the very source of all life, for in the final analysis this applies even to carnivorous animals. The only difference is that the carnivores obtain the natural energies stored in plants second-hand, while the vegetarian animals receive them directly. Man also, whether he eats vegetables and fruit or animals, draws his vitality from the same vegetable world, which in turn springs from the soil.

Trees are the highest example of the vegetable kingdom. Unlike human beings or animals, they function in every sphere. Their roots are in the lithosphere and are always in contact with the hydrosphere through the circulation of water in the earth, their trunks and branches are in the atmosphere, and their foliage receives radiation from the stratosphere. The foliage also receives other cosmic rays falling on our planet and is in contact with atmospheric vapor and moisture, which come to it in the form of rain. Throughout the whole of its growing period the work of a tree is incessant. Its thousands of leaves constantly evaporate and breathe out water into the atmosphere, while the whole surface of the leaves is continually absorbing the maximum quantity of solar energy. The leaves also take in nitrogen from the atmosphere and various other elements and radiations, which they accumulate and elaborate by means of their millions of chlorophyll cells. No other living thing draws into itself vitality from such universal sources; therefore trees make the greatest contribution to physical life on this planet.

Despite the fact that his very existence is dependent upon them, man has abused this greatest gift and through his folly has sadly upset the balance of Nature.

Primitive man lived by the forest, but when new desires were created he cleared it, thus removing the source of his natural food, and started an artificial way of life. His new habits were contagious and spread with ever-increasing momentum round the earth, until today few regions are to be found where Nature reigns. Some virgin forests may still be found in the North and South Americas, along the Pacific Coast, in some islands of the Pacific, and in Russia. But in the greater part of the world the forests have been removed or invaded and their soil has been depleted.

Resulting from unnatural industries, from war, and from greed, the modern world has reached such a degree of mechanism that the soil of one part of the earth is transported to another to feed those who make no contribution themselves to its fertility. In the early days of World War II, people were shocked at the reports that the Germans were sending trainloads of good black earth from Czechoslovakian forests each day into Germany to reinforce the worked-out lands of their own country. But little does the public realize that this process has been going on throughout the world for the past century. For instance, when the early settlers found themselves in the newly discovered continent of Australia, they took to sheep farming and wheat growing because they could make big money from these. Their flocks grazed on virgin lands and they felled the forest to extend their farms. They exported their wheat and wool harvests to other lands and with them their land's fertility. As the market boomed their flocks and farms increased and soon the sparse covering of grass was overgrazed and the thin layer of topsoil worn away, exported in the form of wheat, wool, and mutton.

It took rather longer for the United States of America and Canada to export the fertility of the Middle West. For the greater part they had deep, rich black loam which they could plow for miles without meeting any obstruction. Other areas were cleared of the forest and planted to corn and this in turn was exported. Nothing was returned to the soil. Year after year these pioneers gnawed into the deep, rich black loam which had been built up by Nature through the centuries and sent it across the oceans in return for gold. That gold would not return the humus to their land nor help them to play fair to the earth. The gold received by those who sold their soil was but a mere pittance by comparison with the cost of rehabilitating their land.

The taking of food from the topsoil and failing to return it in compost is suicidal. Western man has been undermining his very existence since the introduction of chemical manures and water sanitation. He has been raping the earth, taking from it crops of every kind, and has failed to recognize the law of return and fair play. Few people realize that every ton of wheat grain represents four fifths of a ton of earth. Vast quantities of topsoil are, as it were, moved in ships from one country to another. Where does this go? Surely some country must be benefiting from such imports. In so far as this produce is fed to livestock, it may be returned to the land as farmyard manure; but the great majority of food consumed by city dwellers eventually leaves their bodies in the form of solid and liquid waste and is lost to the land, owing to modern sewage.

Addressing the first Men of the Trees Summer School at Oxford in 1938, Sir Albert Howard, C.I.E., M.A., in his paper on "The Floor of the Forest," said:

> In the forest the processes of decay and the processes of growth always balance one another. The vegetable waste, together with the by-products of the large animal population which every piece of woodland maintains, form an

intimate mixture on the floor of the forest. . . . In dealing with its own wastes, the forest creates none of the problems with which mankind in similar circumstances is constantly struggling—smells, flies, dustbins, infectious diseases, the disposal of water-borne sewage, town and other councils, an army of officials, more and more rates, and a growing burden of debt. The forest is the perfect sanitarian, the supreme chemist and economist.

And again, in his recent book, *The Maintenance of Soil Fertility in Great Britain,* Sir Albert draws attention to one of the most destructive stupidities of pseudo science which for 300 years has been ruining the fertility of the whole British Empire. He says:

By far the most important demand of the Industrial Revolution was the creation of two new hungers—the hunger of a rapidly increasing urban population and the hunger of its machines. Both needed the things raised on the land: both have seriously depleted the reserves of fertility in our soils. Neither of these hungers has been accompanied by the return of the respective wastes to the land. Instead, vast sums of money were spent in completely side-tracking these wastes and preventing their return to the land which so sorely needed them. Much ingenuity was devoted to developing an effective method of removing the human wastes to the rivers and seas. These finally took the shape of our present water-borne sewage system. The contents of the dustbins of house and factory first found their way into huge dumps, and then into incinerators or into refuse tips sealed by a thin covering of cinders or soil.

If all the humus formed from waste matter from millions of cases of oranges and apples, millions of tons of beef and mutton, wheat, and oil, were used, how fertile the land would be. Britain has been notorious for waste and improvidence and the famine conditions with which she is now confronted are the result of ignorance and wastefulness.

It behooves the British, as the greatest food importers in the world, to reverse the process and set an example in conservation.

The Men of the Trees, after twenty-five years of endeavor, are at length beginning to discern a change in the attitude of the general public. There is a growing appreciation of trees, not only for their beauty, but for the vital contribution that they make to life. Outstanding among the new voices is an English farmer who is making an appeal for more enlightenment among farmers throughout the world, asking them for a more generous treatment of the tree, which can render such a great service to agriculture.

The productive capacity of the soil depends on trees and agriculture is dependent on forestry: the one devoted to the planting, conservation, and harvesting of trees, and the other to grains, fruits, vegetables, and animals. Fish, game, and honey may be considered as secondary forest crops. The honey bee is one of the greatest gifts to the farm and forest, for it fertilizes not only the farm crops, but also the flowers of trees.

Every farm contains land that will not produce farm crops, but no land is of such poor quality that it will not support tree growth. If the farmer will only recognize the value of the trees to himself and the importance of the forest to the country and to mankind in general, he will undertake to grow crops of trees with as much care and forethought as he spends on producing other crops. Forestry and agriculture are complementary and may be practiced on the same farm. The forest provides fuel and construction timber, fence posts, and wood for implements, and, while growing, the trees provide shelter for stock and nesting places for helpful birds that destroy harmful insects. Forestry, too, helps in the economy of the farm by providing employment in the winter, thus enabling a farmer to maintain a larger permanent staff of farm-forest workers throughout the year.

Above all, forests increase the fertility of the land. It is possible by planting unproductive areas or the lower grades of farmland to improve their quality. With the exception of steep hillsides or sand, all land can be brought within the range of agriculture through the improvement of the soil made possible by the leaf fall and irrigation of forest trees. It is therefore evident that the economy of forestry and that of agriculture are intimately connected. So close is this integration that when a farmer suddenly sells his entire wood crop and removes his hedgerow timber, a severe threat is made upon the economy of the farm. To fell all the trees on a property is often a prelude to disaster. In many parts of the world, farm abandonment and the decline of agriculture have coincided with forest destruction.

The objection often raised to tree planting is that one has to wait too long to reap the harvest, whereas the farmer is able to produce an annual crop and thus have an annual income. The forester, on the other hand, may have to wait the whole of his life before his harvest is ripe. This, indeed, is a strong argument in favor of farmers practicing forestry. On considering the question more closely, however, there are short-rotation tree crops, such as willows for basketmaking, which, when once established, can be harvested every year. In England, cricket-bat willows have been found to be a profitable investment, yielding returns in ten or twelve years. There are also fast-growing species of poplar which are now being planted in several parts of the world, where they will bring returns in from twenty to thirty years, and, while growing, yield valuable sets each year which can be disposed of for cash or used to extend the farm plantation. In the case of many tree crops, there are incidental products during the growth of the wood crop: for instance, syrup and sugar from maple, various gums and resins—such as turpentine and rosin—cones, faggots, berries, wild honey, fruit, nuts, fish, and game. Unlike farm crops, the forest provides its own fertilizer through the annual fall of its leaves, bark, and twigs. Inorganic fertilizers are never applied, nor are poison sprays needed; in fact, the forest is self-supporting and is a complete biological unit.

The home woods on a farm can maintain that balance of Nature so essential to productivity and the well-being of man and beast. A forest or wood is not merely an aggregation of trees, but a living community. The interrelation and inter-dependence among man, plants, fungi, animals, birds, and insects is great, yet it is often overlooked in farming and forestry plans. No farm is complete without its balanced home wood, where so many good influences are at work. No forest or home wood can contribute its best unless it contains a mixture of species, both broad-leaved and coniferous trees. Pure stands of conifers tend to make the ground acid and fail to provide litter with soil-improving properties. This may be accounted for by the fact that the micro-fauna of the soil is poorer under pines than under mixed hardwoods, and the number of earthworms is less and their weight but a third of those found in the soil of the natural woods. Moreover, pine woods are inhospitable to birds and wild life. Lacking browse, deer are liable to bark the trees, and squirrels and grouse de-stroy the buds. When a pure coniferous forest is artificially created, the balance of Nature is disturbed. Birds may forsake the area owing to absence of food and thus permit insect pests to establish themselves unmolested. Insectivorous birds are the friends of both the farmer and the forester and are well known to be important controls of farm and forest insects.

As among human beings, so with trees, prevention is better than cure. If we are to avoid the disastrous outbreaks which have ravaged Continental forests, we must adopt a long-sighted, comprehensive, and permanent policy which will control the injurious fauna and prevent their ever becoming pests.

Protection may be natural and indirect, or artificial and direct. The first can be achieved by good silviculture, by pro-viding conditions for the most favorable growth and at the same time producing an unfavorable state for the develop-ment of the parasite and plunderer. The best way, if not the only way, to achieve this is by careful and correct choice of species, composition, or mixtures, method of regeneration, and after-treatment. The silvicultural method is most successful against physical damage by windfall, fire, frost, or snow, but only partially effective against fungi and insects, and of less use in practice against injurious birds and animals. These must be dealt with by biological control—that is to say, by the active encouragement of beneficial agents and the suppression of their enemies. The encouragement of useful insects or the introduction of parasites on harmful ones is difficult and sometimes dangerous, because the balance of Nature is so fine in adjustment that it can easily be upset. There is a classical instance of this in the case of the Kootenay scale on oranges. The growers in California had heard of the success of the Australian ladybirds, and imported a quantity into their groves with great success. The Florida growers thought they would do likewise, and ordered a supply of these same ladybirds from California, which duly arrived with sufficient scale to keep them happy in transit. The remainder of this, together with the ladybirds, was turned loose in the groves of Florida. In a very short time the Florida growers observed a new kind of scale which quickly spread throughout the country, causing a vast amount of damage, while their original pest did not prove to be the right food for that particular kind of ladybird. The reduction of the new pest took them several years, at the cost of millions of dollars.

Another instance of failure of the biological method was when weasels were sent from Norfolk, England, to Australia, with a view to reducing the ravages of rabbits in that country. Very soon Norfolk became overrun with rabbits and to this day they are still increasing. As in many other parts of the country, they are proving to be one of the most injurious pests known to the farmer and forester, and costing the country something in the neighborhood of 70 millions a year.

The encouragement of predacious birds for the control of harmful insects is easier than that of useful insects, and is something with which everyone can help. It should be remembered that there are two factors only which govern the decrease of any organism—lack of food and the presence of enemies. Insects and animals can be controlled biologically by means of other insects and parasitic fungi. All parasites are characterized by their almost complete interdependence on one species or genus of insect. They can control their numbers, but not annihilate them; they are the police rather than the military force in Nature. Moreover, from their mode of life it is readily understood that parasites cannot by themselves check any sudden increase of injurious insects, for their generation is always one stage, usually one year, behind that of their hosts. Parasitic insects must be regarded as an ever-present and necessary form of natural control, which it is only possible to encourage by the discouragement of its enemies.

In England the starling is one of the most useful birds all the year round, but especially in summer.

Collinge gives as its adult food: injurious insects 26.5 per cent, beneficial insects 2.5 per cent; nestlings: ground beetles 7.2 per cent, *Mellonthinae* 13.5 per cent, various weevils 3.7 per cent, lepidopterous larvae 39.3 per cent, and as the fledgling period is about twenty days and the young are visited from 250 to 350 times a day, the number of injurious insects consumed is very great. The results from the judicious use of nesting boxes on the Continent have been so successful that in all well-managed woods where natural sites are probably very limited, a great deal can be accomplished by providing suitable nesting boxes. I have no fault to find with the starling, except that he will often sit or swing on the leading shoot of a Sitka spruce until it breaks or is seriously injured.

The redstart is a beneficial bird of considerable importance, since it is readily encouraged to nest in artificial sites. The robin can also be encouraged by the provision of suitable nesting boxes. It is common in woods, where it feeds almost entirely on insects obtained from the ground and foliage. Other closely allied species are the blackcap, grasshopper warbler, garden warbler, and nightingale.

The arboreal warblers form a very valuable check on the numbers of small defoliatory larvae and to a less extent of *Rhyncophoia*. These warblers feed largely on the adult and egg stages and so their utility is increased. The blue tit, unfortunately, is almost restricted to broad-leaved trees and is of primary importance specially with *Rhynchota*, particularly the "woolly" chermes, the felted beech coccus, and the ash and willow scale. The coal tit is a true forest species, and because of its other characteristics is the most useful member of the genus. It is seen searching the trunks of trees, and also comes to the ground to search for pupae concealed in the grass. The marsh tit, although less useful, is distinctly beneficial. The willow tit is of great importance because of its preference for *Coleoptera* and the small bud and needle-infesting *Lepidoptera*. The long-tailed tit is of restricted utility on account of its habitat, but of primary importance, especially, when it wanders in winter. The goldcrest, which inhabits all kinds of coniferous woods, particularly of spruce and Douglas fir, but not young plantations, is entirely arboreal and lives principally on insects and spiders obtained from twigs and needles. The great tit's usefulness is due to its constant search for *Rhynchota*, which are its staple food, and it feeds on them throughout the winter. These birds must destroy enormous numbers of *Chermesidae*. To encourage them in woods devoid of unsound timber, nesting boxes must be provided to induce most tits to nest. Their enemy, the sparrowhawk, should be destroyed.

Woodpeckers are often accused of damaging trees, but evidence shows that they rarely, if ever, attack or disfigure healthy timber. The cuckoo is of great value to forestry. Unlike other birds, cuckoos are not forced to remain in particular areas for nesting purposes, and are therefore free to move about wherever food is most abundant. They search all types of vegetation for larval forms and it has been estimated that 100 cuckoos can account for over 2½ million *Scolytidae* of the *Coleoptera* family in fifteen days. The nightjar is of first importance, particularly on newly reclaimed areas, where cockchafer and bark-beetle pests are likely to be severe. Gamekeepers frequently shoot the nightjar for a hawk.

Owls are good foresters. The long-eared owl destroys rats, mice, voles, and small rabbits. The tawny owl, found in broad-leaved woods, feeds on long-tailed mice, shrews, grass mice, water voles, and rabbits. It is one of the most useful birds in the British Isles. The barn owl and the little owl are of less importance and sometimes destroy other useful birds.

It is important to appreciate the value of systematic, as opposed to chance, methods of forest protection. Continental foresters have learned by bitter experience the result of the neglect of biological control in their artificial plantations and woodlands. British farmers must not fall into the same errors, but must learn from their mistakes. It seems that they are taking no more precautions than the German foresters did seventy or eighty years ago. The fact that till now they have suffered little tends to make them serenely content. The importance of action now has been heightened by the extensive felling of timber. Often lop and top and unwanted trees have been left in the woods, dead and dying timber has been untouched, while the best has been taken. Unless precautionary measures are adopted, the country may be swept with pests, causing the destruction and disappearance of the few woodlands and plantations that remain.

The biological control of enemies by predatory birds and animals may be of limited practical application. It is thoroughly economic, however, to take steps to encourage the natural enemies of voles and mice, for, as in the case of insects, it is important to exclude these animals from the forest. They are so small and subject to such prodigious increase that artificial control is out of the question. The cost of artificial control is many times that of silvicultural and biological control. Continental experience shows costly failures. In Bavaria in one year alone the expense of artificial protection, leaving out of account the loss of timber involved, was estimated at $400,-000. In America whole tree species have been swept from the woods by diseases, even though large sums of money were spent on artificial measures in an attempt to control or eradicate. It has been said that if all the birds were removed from any country, in two years' time it would be impossible to grow any farm crop, despite the many chemical insecticides of these modern days. The good forester will place nesting boxes to attract helpful birds, and farmers will do well to plant and protect hedgerow timber to provide nesting places for their feathered friends.

Birds are great distributors of tree seeds, especially those with fleshy fruits; jays have been known to plant acorns.

There have been cases where birds have exerted injurious influences upon forests, but this is usually where the natural balance has been disturbed by man. I have observed a case where almost the entire crop of seeds of a pine forest was destroyed by blackbirds and other birds. They preferred to take the seed from burned areas, where it was exposed on the soil. Large birds, such as pigeons, may break the leading shoots of trees, especially those of the tallest trees in a plantation, which serve them as look-outs. The concentration of starlings or sparrows continually roosting in trees may be injurious to their growth. Birds have been known to distribute forest pests, such as the seeds of *Ribes,* the intermediate host of the white-pine blister, but on the whole the good that birds do far outweighs the harm.

Squirrels, by eating the bark round white-pine-blister rust cankers, may reduce the volume of spores infecting the *Ribes* host plants. Rodents are notorious seed eaters, but at the same time they do help to distribute seed. I have seen a beech hedge along the bottom of a bank entirely planted by squirrels. They had stored the mast and forgotten to eat it.

Harmful fungi are better known than their helpful relations. Some of the helpful ones provide, as it were, a "living bridge" for conducting the nutriment in the soil through their cellular threads to the feeding rootlets of the plant or tree. These symbiotic fungi are formed in humus by the great majority of our farm plants and forest trees. These are known as mycorhiza formers. If a healthy young pine or oak is lifted from the soil, a white fungus in the form of threads will be observed, attached to the hair roots of the little tree. At first sight it looks as though the tree has been attacked by root fungus, while in fact this particular fungus is fulfilling a most useful purpose. Indeed, young trees, whether oak, beech, larch, pine, or spruce, would not thrive without the help of this useful fungoid growth, for it helps to prepare the plant food and bring it into a condition in which it can better be assimilated through the feeding roots of the plant or tree. The presence of toadstools in the woods is an outward and visible sign that the mycorhiza is at work. Nature has provided the roots of forest trees with a very remarkable organization. In the absence of humus there is no mycorhiza and growth is stunted and often diseased; but where natural conditions prevail, abundant mycorhiza ensures the fertility of the soil.

The human body is the earth in miniature. For is it not true that each part of the body is dependent on the other? If any part becomes defective or is lost, the whole balance is upset. And so it is with the earth. For millions of years the earth has built up and maintained its unique routine, which is now threatened. Let man go forward in partnership with Nature and use his accumulated knowledge to foster and maintain this essential balance.

9.

FORESTRY IN RUSSIA

THE SOVIET UNION has the responsibility of the largest forest area in the world. About thirty-eight per cent of the total land surface is classed as forest. It is to her credit that Russia started on a conservative forest policy long before any apparent necessity arose. While other countries were squandering their woodland wealth, this nation was maintaining its forest capital and at the same time becoming one of the largest timber exporters in the world. For many years Leningrad and Archangel have been renowned for the high quality of the timber that has passed through their ports and Leningrad has now been made one of the most efficient and up-to-date ports for handling large quantities of timber.

According to the figures, which were kindly obtained for me from Moscow in October, 1945, by their London representative, the general forest area of the U.S.S.R. covers 933 million hectares, while the productive forest area covers 652 million hectares. The forest area of the Soviet Union may be divided into two main groups. In the first the dominant species are coniferous and consist of 390 million hectares. In the second are the deciduous forests, which cover 130 million hectares, while 132 million hectares remain unclassified.

It is interesting to note that out of 180 million hectares of developed forest, 74 million hectares are set aside, unfelled, for purposes of water preservation.

Stocks of standing timber are reckoned at 41 milliard cubic meters, and of these 35 milliard cubic meters are coniferous and 6 milliard cubic meters deciduous.

Of the estimated annual wood increment of 650 million cubic meters, only about 300 million cubic meters is cut—in 1940 273.2 million cubic meters were exploited—and of this figure about 150 million cubic meters is marketable timber, excluding firewood.

The greater part of the forest wealth of the Soviet Union is to be found in the distant regions of Siberia and the Far East, the exploitation of which is attended by considerable difficulties. However, in the last few years the main areas for timber production have been changed from the west and central parts of the U.S.S.R. to the north and to Siberia.

The coniferous forests alone comprise about one third of the world's forest lands, for they extend 3600 miles from west to east and 600 miles from north to south. The forests in Asiatic Russia are mainly situated in Siberia. They are very variable in character and contain much *taiga,* or swamp forest, while vast areas have suffered from the ravages of fire.

The following is an extract from *Soviet and Tsarist Siberia* by Dr. George Borodin, published by Rich and Cowan, London:

> Timber for the World! There is enough and to spare in Siberia. And the great point about it is that the Soviet Government is allowing nothing to interfere with its conservation. The policy of the Timber Trust is to ensure that the disasters which have occurred elsewhere in the exploitation of forest land are not repeated. Each year timber authorities, advised by surveyors, schedule so many trees for felling—and not only so many trees, but the actual trees to be cut. This figure is not exceeded. Any forester who cuts down an unscheduled tree is subject to severe penalty. And for every tree cut down, a new one is planted. Thus, by wise planning at every stage, the richest

natural wealth of northern Siberia is being preserved.
There will be no denudation or deforestation, with its
economic consequences and its devastating effect on climate. But the policy in no way restricts the flow of wood
into the mills. The rate of consumption might be dou-
bled, or even trebled—as it may have been under the stress
of war—but there would still be no risk of deforestation.
The areas of England and France put together would not
be sufficient to cover the Siberian forest lands, which are
constantly patrolled and watched, largely from the air, to
preserve them in their best condition.

The northern forest is composed principally of Scots pine
with some admixture of spruce, larch, and fir, and more frequently white birch. Southwards the broad-leaved species are
more apparent, oak becoming the prevailing timber and forming forests with beech, maple, ash, and elm as admixtures. As
the plains are approached, the forests become almost entirely
broad-leaved. The northern slopes of the Crimean mountains
are clothed with oak and the small-leaved hornbeam on the
lower slopes and beech forests on the higher mountains. But
the dry limestone tops of the ranges are treeless. The southern
slopes have many evergreen trees, including the juniper,
cypress, and cedar of Lebanon. The middle slopes are clothed
with oak, and the highest parts with pine. In the Caucasus the
forests are chiefly coniferous, although on the lower slopes
oak, ash, pear, apple, and maple may be found, with alder and
willow in low-lying and damper situations. Beech forests cover
large areas of the upper slopes, and oak, hornbeam, ash, lime,
and maple are common. The beech forests are generally pure,
providing thick canopy and a forest floor covered with mosses,
while in the clearings are found azaleas and thick ferns. The
high mountainsides are covered with the dark green of pine
forests or giant firs, some of which reach a height of 180 feet.
The first recorded attempt to bring the Russian forests under
management is attributed to Michael, founder of the House of
Romanoff, and to Alexis II, who became Tsar in 1645. They,

as a first step, provided protection against theft and fire. The successor of Alexis II, the far-seeing Peter the Great, inaugurated a long-reaching program aimed at the more economic use of wood and the formation of forest reserves. Perhaps it was while he was working as a shipwright in Amsterdam that he found his first love for wood and a desire to build a navy for his own country. During his travels in Germany and other European countries, he probably studied forestry and the laws of conservation, and so returned to his own land equipped for the great task to which he set himself. At all events, on his return to Russia he began to reserve growing stands of ship timber, and all forests for a depth of thirty-five miles along rivers were placed under a newly organized administration of Crown forests. He built his famous Don flotilla on the River Voronezh and used it to assist his southern expansion, for the forests provided the timber for the construction of his ships. Ample regulations were introduced to deal with the economic utilization of timber of all sorts. It is significant that the use of the saw instead of the ax was advocated and enforced.

Although there was a short setback to this good beginning when Peter's wife, Catherine I, influenced by her minister, Menshikoff, abolished the forest administration laws, the situation was saved when these laws were re-enacted under Anna Ivanovna and many new prescriptions for the proper use of wood were added. In 1727 a forest expert, Fökel, was appointed, and reafforestation was inaugurated by the sowing of acorns in the most poorly wooded districts. Planting was enforced, not only in the lands under the administration, but also upon privately owned lands, and, if the owners were neglectful, their lands were confiscated and reafforested by the forest administration. The laws restricting felling were abolished again by Catherine II in 1788 and, much to the concern of the Admiralty, the supply of ship timber was threatened. No further restrictive measures were imposed, however, but rather an ameliorative policy was attempted; for example, prizes for plantations were offered by some provincial governors. When Alexander II abolished serfdom in 1861, he allotted land to the peasants and in some parts as much as from twenty-five to fifty per cent of the forest land was handed over to them. Then followed a general slaughtering of the trees both by peasants and by the private owners who had suffered by losing the services of the serfs.

By 1864 the destruction had become so widespread that a movement for reform was begun by the Tsar, who restricted acreage that might be felled, prohibited clearings, and gave premiums for good management and plantations. In 1875 a special commission was appointed to elaborate a general order, and, after years of hearing testimony and of deliberation, promulgated in 1888 a comprehensive law for the conservation of all forests.

The devastation and its effect on water flow and soil conditions had been most felt in the southern districts adjoining the steppe and these experiences were the immediate cause for the enactment of the forest law which was then framed for the whole of European Russia. This law established that all forests protecting shifting sands and dunes, binding the shores of rivers, canals, and other waters, and those on the slopes of mountains, where they served to prevent landslides, erosion, and avalanches, should be managed by the Crown forest departments under special plans prepared by its forest officers. All forests classed as protective forests were strictly preserved. In other forests clearing for farms was permitted, but this was allowed only if the soil and lie of the land were fit for orchards and vineyards. If the land was fit for farm use, permission was granted for temporary cultivation on the condition that it was eventually reforested. This was allowed, however, only if another formerly farmed parcel of the same size had been re-afforested at least three years before the proposed clearing. These regulations, although very exacting, were carried out in a thoroughly democratic spirit. Local committees were formed in each province and district, composed of various representatives of local administration, including foresters, justices of the peace or other justices, the county council, and two elected forest owners. In all there were from nine to

eleven members, under the presidency of the governor. It was
such committees that decided which areas were to be included
in protective forests. They approved of the working plans for
these forests as well as for the unreserved lands. They determined which clearings might be made and exercised wide
police powers with reference to all forest matters. The forest
administration drew up working plans for the reserve forests
free of cost. The same body of forestry experts prepared working plans for the private owners, who, however, paid for them.
Owners were permitted to prepare their own plans, but they
had to be submitted to their provincial forest committee.

Forestry legislation was not entirely one-sided, for all protective forests were freed from taxes forever. Those artificially
planted were not taxed for thirty years, while any expenses
arising from measures ordered might be charged to the government. Some of the more expert forest officials were detailed to
give free advice to forest owners. Prizes were given for the
best results of silviculture operations. On the recommendation
of the forest committees, medals, money rewards, and other
distinctions were given to the forest guards and forest man-
agers of private as well as public forests. Plants were distributed free or at cost price and working plans for protective
forests were made free of charge. Long-term loans could be
arranged through the Imperial Loan Bank on condition that
conservative management was assured. In a single year 7 million acres were in this way mortgaged under such management.

In Russia, forestry education goes back as far as 1782, when
a number of foresters were imported from Germany to take
charge of the forest management and train foresters. Each
Forstmeister had six pupils assigned to him. This method apparently failed to produce results, and, so because of the great
interest in ship timber, a course in forestry was started at the
Naval Academy in 1800. The growing need of foresters led to
the formation of separate forestry schools at Zarskoye Selo, at
Kozlov, and at Saint Petersburg. This last absorbed the other
two and became the first Forest Institute. Soon it had as many
as fifteen professors and instructors conducting a four-year

course, preparing students for the higher positions in the forestry service. Other forestry schools followed, and ten secondary schools were established for rangers and under-foresters. By the beginning of the twentieth century the number of schools had increased to thirty. These were boarding schools in the woods, where a certain number of students were taught free of charge. The course of two years was mainly directed to practical work and theoretical study in silviculture.

Forestry experimental stations were set up in various parts of the country by the Administration of Crown Lands, and a very considerable and advanced literature is evidence of the good education and activity of the forest service. Two main forestry journals and several lesser ones kept the profession informed. There were several societies for the encouragement of silviculture. Probably the oldest was the Imperial Russian Society for the Advancement of Forestry. This was founded in 1832, and remained active until 1850. It published a journal and translated foreign books, among which was *Forest Mathematics,* by the noted German forester König, who later prepared yield tables for the Society, based, not on the growth of a single tree, but on entire stands per acre classified by species. These yield tables were the first of their kind ever produced and foresters the world over are today indebted to the far-sightedness of this old Russian society for the pioneer work done by König. The first society for professional foresters was founded in Saint Petersburg as far back as 1871. There was another in Moscow and others were founded later.

Theodor Karlowitsch Arnold was outstanding among the early Russian writers and practitioners, and is recognized as the father of Russian forestry. He was the soul of the forest organization work, and, first as professor and afterwards as Director of the Institute for Agronomy and Forestry at Moscow, he finally became head of the forest department in the Ministry of Appanages, where he remained until his death in 1902. Arnold was the author of several classical works on silviculture, forest mensuration, and forest management. In conjunction with Dr. W. A. Tichonoff, he published an encyclopaedic work in three volumes. In the first volume, *Russia's Forest,* the author made an extended plea for improved forestry practice. In 1895 he published a history of forestry in Germany, France, and Russia.

Among other prominent foresters who have advanced forestry in Russia should be mentioned Count Vargaci de Bedemar, who made the first attempt to prepare Russian growth and yield tables in the middle of the nineteenth century. Professor A. F. Rudzsky devoted volumes to the mathematical branches and methods of forest organization. The names of Tursky, Kravchinsky, and Kaigodorov are known to Russian students of dendrology and silviculture, and, among a later generation, those of Morozov, Nestorov, Orlov, and Tolsky may be mentioned. Russian investigators have become prominent in the natural sciences, and the work of the soil physicists Otozky and Dokuchaev are familiar to foresters.

The Russians were among the first to study the fundamentals of erosion control. Great was the success that attended the early planting of trees for shelter belts by immigrants who settled in the steppe region in the early nineteenth century. Later plantings between 1880 and 1886 were on such a spectacular scale, with such excellent results, that a special Government commission was appointed to study afforestation on the steppes. The objectives placed before the commission included the protection of farms from wind, aid in the ripening of grain, more uniform distribution and retention of snow, raising the water table, modification of temperature, the attraction of rain, raising the productivity of unused lands, and control of soil erosion and drifting sands.

The Bureau of Deserts of the U.S.S.R. Institute of Plant Industry is making a special study of the reclamation of all the Russian deserts, of which the largest area is in Central Asia. The reclamation of shifting sands and sand dunes has received considerable attention; also, to some extent, the reboisement of mountain slopes in the Crimea and the Caucasus. Of the former, some 10 million acres were completed, and 1500 square miles of swamps in Western Russia were reclaimed by the formation of extensive canals, and reclothed with meadow and forest.

As in the United States and Canada, so in the U.S.S.R., the black earth lands are subject to soil erosion caused by the action of the wind or by occasional heavy downpours of rain during the dry summers. It has been estimated that during the last twenty-five years 135 million acres of fertile black earth have been so removed and replaced by river sand. The Soviet Government has established a research station at Novosil, in the province of Tula, to deal with this problem. The obvious remedy has been found to be tree planting, and where this has been done on a large scale it has been found that the yield of grain and grasses has increased considerably. Tree planting has also been found to prevent the extension of gullies and ravines and during the last twelve years nearly a million acres of new woods have been planted by the farmers in the U.S.S.R. The Russians were among the first to plant shelter belts as windbreaks in the steppes, and their valuable pioneer work in finding the most suitable species has made a considerable contribution to that particular kind of reclamation work, so necessary in Australia, Canada, and the United States. The Russians have had a great deal of experience in planting shifting sands and sand deserts which were cultivated within historic times. Much is being done today to control the deserts by planting suitable vegetation on the sands, gradually establishing a green cover which will stop their movement. The *saksaul* tree, used for fuel, has been extensively planted, and apricot, wormwood, and the rubber-bearing plant *kok-sagyz* are being successfully grown.

The Russians have gigantic plans for land reclamation and rehabilitation, but World War II made vast inroads into their forests, and now, with the millions of homeless in that great country, still further timber must be sacrificed to build houses. An ever-increasing planting program will be required, not only to provide lumber for the rapidly growing population, but as a safeguard against erosion. The vast majority of the inhabitants of the U.S.S.R. in the past have always been closely associated with farm and forest and their inherent patriotism will doubtless enable them to continue in their conservative ways and set an example which all the world may follow.

10.

SILVICULTURE IN CENTRAL EUROPE

EVERY country in Europe has made its own particular contribution to silviculture. The study of the development of the science of forestry in Europe shows man's progressive use of land throughout the centuries. Consciously or unconsciously, the most economic methods have been adopted and here the art of silviculture has reached the highest and most intensive application. There are countries in Europe in which we can follow all the phases of development through which newer countries have passed, or else will eventually have to pass, in the story of their evolution. We can witness successive generations of Europeans who have, by trial and error, by research and experiment, and by hard necessity managed the adjustment of dense human occupation of the land without destruction of the land's productive capacity. Down throughout the ages the forest has been an essential feature in the problem of land utilization and has profoundly influenced not only a country's own well-being, but that of the peoples of other countries of the world who have followed the example of European practice.

Germany is known among foresters as the fatherland of forestry. This country has long been regarded by informed observers as the most advanced in the science of silviculture.

101

For many years it was my privilege to study forestry throughout Central Europe, originally in company with my fellow
students and later when conducting parties of foresters and
research students under the direction of Continental professors
of forestry.

To the French belong the credit for having first recognized
the indirect benefits of the forest, such as its influence on
climate, its water-conserving effects, and its aesthetical and
general cultural influences and values. It was Leonardo da
Vinci who first interested Louis XII in forestry, which resulted
in the birth of European silvicultural systems. Leonardo's interest in growing trees may have been prompted by his research into the properties of wood, for it was he who invented
the first key for the identification of timbers. When I was preparing a key for the identification of European woods, I found
I could not do better than take Leonardo da Vinci's key as a
basis for my work.

The conservation movement, which started in France, was
well established by the end of the eighteenth century, but it
was not until the end of the first quarter of the nineteenth
century that this movement made any impression on Germany.
However, the roots of German forestry reach back beyond the
Middle Ages and traces may be found as far back as 1000
years before Christ. It was then that Aryan tribes from Central
Asia began to overrun the country. These belonged to the
Celtic or Gaelic race, which had gradually come to occupy
part of France, Spain, Northern Italy, the western part
of Germany, and the British Isles. These were followed
by the Germani, meaning "neighbor" or "brother," also
Aryan tribes, who appeared at the Black Sea about 1000 B.C.
and in Switzerland and Belgium about 100 B.C. These were
followed by the Slovenes and the Slovaks, or Wends, who took
land left by the Germani. These early settlers found the mountainsides clothed with evergreen or broad-leaved trees, but their
first thought was to make clearings for farms and fields for
herding their cattle. Soon they began to suffer from drought,
and some of the tribes were faced with famine. Tradition

relates how they called upon their gods for rain, but their prayers were of little avail. After a time some of the tribesmen made the discovery that on the other side of the hills, where the slopes were still green with trees, the rain fell in abundance. Their provident instinct prompted them wisely to leave covering on the hills so that the fertility of the valleys might be retained. Their inherent reverence for trees was revived.

Sir James Frazer has shown that tree worship was well established in all the great European families of Aryan stock. Amongst the Celts, the oak worship of the Druids is familiar to everyone, and their old word for sanctuary seems to be identical in origin and meaning with the Latin *nemus,* a grove or woodland glade. Sacred groves were common among the ancient Germans and severe were the penalties exacted for damaging the bark of growing trees, or felling protective groves. The native regard for woods and forests prevented the inhabitants of these countries from committing wholesale destruction, and their love of the chase caused them to create forest reserves. Indeed, by the end of the eighth century the word *Forst,* which until then had been used merely to denote the King's property, was exclusively used to designate any territory in which the hunt had been reserved. Not all the areas called *Forst* were woodland, for real woodlands were known as *silva,* or *nemus.*

The beginnings of German silviculture have been traced back long before the Middle Ages, when the so-called *Hackwaldbetrieb* system of alternate field crops and oak coppice was introduced in the Oldenwald, in the valley of Sieg, in the Saar, and along the Moselle River. In some of the thickly settled parts of Western Germany and Austria the forests came under production as early as the twelfth and thirteenth centuries.

The discovery that conifers could be easily introduced over large areas led to the early introduction of a clear-cutting system which preserved single trees or groups of seed trees, the minimum number of which was prescribed. Under the influence of Hartig (1764–1837), organizer of the Prussian State

Forest Service, the Germans developed the orthodox high-forest management of beech, the so-called shelter-wood system. The same system was adopted a little later in the spruce forests, owing to the severe damage from windfall. Thus it gradually came about that a large part of the German forests were clear-cut and planted in the latter half of the nineteenth century. The methods of artificial regeneration varied. Plantations of conifers were made from the seventeenth century. Ball planting of pine was recommended in Prussia in the latter half of the eighteenth century. Other methods of artificial regeneration included mound planting, *Hügelpflanzung,* and wedge planting, *Klemmpflanzung.* Up to the end of the eighteenth century the number of species was limited to the indigenous varieties such as oak, beech, pine, larch, and spruce, but these foresters were looking for rapidly growing species to restock the devastated and open portions of their forests. The German troops who fought in the American War of Independence brought home the knowledge of many fast-growing exotics, and, stimulated by a few enthusiasts, large numbers of foreign trees were experimented with; but it was found that the climatic and soil requirements were not sufficiently well known to make them succeed. Only *Pinus strobus, Quercus rubra,* and *Fraxinus americana* have survived out of the many plantations made at the time.

It was not until the first half of the nineteenth century that the sustained-yield principle dominated the German system of forest management. It was progress, indeed, to have reached this high ideal; but when, after the Industrial Revolution, wood had changed from a carefully rationed, essential material to an ordinary commodity, the production of which came to be governed largely by financial considerations, the forests were prostituted for profit. Conifers produced the best financial returns, and in consequence they were grown more and more, to the exclusion of broad-leaved trees. Certainly there was at first an increase in the financial returns, but the even-aged plantations of a single species were contrary to Nature. Before long serious defects were obvious: there was soil deterioration and decreased rate of growth. This system of monoculture lessened the trees' resistance to animal and plant parasites and increased the risk to injuries from snow break and wind.

Not until foresters began to gain a better knowledge of the natural sciences was the policy reversed. It was Professor Karl Gayer, silviculturist at the University of Munich, who in the last quarter of the nineteenth century led a new school of thought which revived some of the practical common sense that had been forgotten in the rush for financial returns. Gayer demanded that the forest be treated in accordance with biological laws instead of the schematic culture of pure stands. He advocated the reintroduction of broad-leaved species, especially beech, and natural regeneration, instead of clear cutting with artificial seeding or planting; the uneven-aged form of forest in place of even-aged stands was part of his teaching. His influence instigated one of the most promising developments of forestry in Germany. Of course, there were mixed hardwood forests that survived the craze for conifers; for instance, in the Spessardt district of Germany I have walked for two and a half days through fine forests of oak and beech which had been run on a 320-year rotation for centuries.

Some European countries have been slow in learning from Germany's mistakes and they are liable slavishly to follow outworn German systems now discarded in the country of their origin. A tragic example of this may be seen in Britain, where the countryside is being ruined by monocultures. Large areas have been afforested with even-aged plantations of a single species, chosen because it was fast-growing or especially suitable for pit props, without paying heed to the natural factors that control the life of the forest. Britain is not the only country to have fallen into this error, which proved to be costly enough to Germany half a century ago, and this should be a lesson for the rest of the world, too.

Austrian forestry has been influenced by German thought to a large degree, but it has not followed the mathematical systems of the Fatherland too strictly. When I was visiting the forests of Austria I was impressed by the flexibility of their silvicultural systems. They were adverse to stem mixtures, but planted in groups following the contour of the land. They planted the moist pockets with moisture-loving species and the steep hillsides with alpine varieties. Their working plans were frequently revised in the light of what they learned from practical experience. These Austrian foresters were artists rather than economists, and they carried on much research in the most advanced forest practice. An important branch of Austrian forestry was carried out by the forest protective service, which consisted of the reboisement of mountains for the regulation of torrential streams. One of the best examples of the spirit of the Austrian policy and of the methods of forest organization and administration is to be found in the provinces of Bosnia and Herzegovina. A survey showed the forest area to be 6¼ million acres, fifty-one per cent of the land area. The most notable work of the Austrian foresters for the past seventy-five years was that of reafforesting the Karst or wastelands in the mountain and hill country of Istria, Trieste, Dalmatia, Montenegro, and adjacent territory skirting the Adriatic Sea. It is a dry limestone country of close to a million acres, stony and rough. Originally it was well forested with hardwoods and conifers and for ages it furnished ship timber and other wood supplies to the Venetians. Through reckless cutting, burning, and pasturing by the small farmers, it had become almost entirely denuded. For centuries countless laws were passed to stop the progress of devastation, without effect; but thanks to the initiative of the Austrian Government and the Forestry Association of that country, these areas are now under forest management.

In Czechoslovakia I was impressed by the enthusiasm of many large landowners who made forestry not only their hobby, but their life's work. They had built up rural industries and had formed prosperous communities working the products of the forest. Forestry requires particular skill in the mountainous region of the northwestern part of that country. To reduce the speed of the wind and the consequent risk of windfalls, rides are cut up the mountainsides dividing compartments of growing trees. The foresters explained to me that the size of each compartment was controlled by a series of factors which checked the speed of hurricanes. By providing correctly placed vents in the form of open rides, they could reduce the speed of the wind to a point of safety. Although much of this is coniferous country, I saw the finest beech forest in Europe in Czechoslovakia.

Every country has a different approach to the science of silviculture. In Switzerland the forests are regarded as most important for the part that they play in preventing avalanches and for holding the soil on the mountainsides. The total forest area of Switzerland is 1,029,000 hectares, which corresponds approximately to twenty-five per cent of the total area of the country. There are no virgin forests, because all forests are worked on an intensive yield basis. The only exception to this rule is made by a number of forestry reserves, which are placed under the supervision of a special government department and in which any cutting down of trees is forbidden. An example is the Swiss National Park in the Engadine, with an area of 16,000 hectares. The majority of the cultivated areas were gradually gained from the erstwhile wooded territory. The relations between agriculture and forestry are generally good. The farmers are very often themselves owners of forests, or interested directly in the administration of publicly owned forests. Experience has taught them that excessive exploitation of forests is always prejudicial to crops which are efficiently protected by forests against rapid changes of temperature, against violent winds, desiccation, and frosts.

Belgium is a splendid example of an industrial country which has retained interest in its forests. The total forest area at the last census, which was taken in 1929, was 541,140 hectares, or approximately 2089 square miles. This area represents almost eighteen per cent of the land surface of the country. It is significant that 341,347 hectares carry broad-leaved trees and only 199,793 hectares coniferous. The species used for artificial reafforestation are spruce, Scots and Corsican pine, and Japanese larch. There are beautiful natural forests of beech in Belgium, one of the finest of which is located a little way out of Brussels—Forêt de Soignies, near Trevune. Near here, too, is one of the most outstanding forestry arboretums in Europe. It was created largely by prisoners of war during the World War I, through the skill of a well-known Belgian forester who persuaded the Germans to allow him to carry out this work. Instead of planting individual trees, as is usual in an ordinary arboretum, they planted groups of trees of a single species over a large area and each year these groups were enlarged until the whole converged to make a forest.

Of the total land area of the Netherlands, namely, 3,298,629 hectares, only 258,482 hectares, or nearly eight per cent, is forest. In the beginning of the nineteenth century practically all woods consisted of foliage trees. Since then the Scots pine has won ground, as this species is particularly suitable for afforestation of poor wasteland. The Dutch found that the establishment of pine forests was neither difficult nor expensive, and the large demand for mine props in the second half of the nineteenth century also stimulated the extension of these forests. It was some time before the people became aware of the importance of afforestation; but in the second half of the nineteenth century fear arose that the larger proportion of all forests in the country would soon disappear, and the conviction established itself that a permanent forest policy, directed or supervised by the government, represented a national interest. In 1888 some farseeing private persons established the Netherlands Heath Society, following the example of Denmark. The society did much for the reclamation of wasteland and also promoted afforestation. In 1897 the government revised the policy of selling common and Crown lands, an act was passed for the purchase of 2000 hectares of blowing sands and heath at Kootwijk, and the Heath Society was charged with the afforestation of this area. It was not until 1899 that the Government Forestry Service was inaugurated, for the purpose of administering the government-owned forests and to afforest wasteland. In 1907 the service was empowered to un-

dertake afforestation on behalf of municipalities, and, if necessary, give financial assistance. In 1922 a new Forestry Act was
enforced, to widen the powers of the Government in this province, and in 1928 a law was passed for the protection of
beauty spots. Since the service was established, over 20,000 hectares of new forests have been planted, mostly on waste soil
of which only a small proportion was already wooded.

The people of the Duchy of Luxembourg are proud of their
trees, and it was under the French Revolutionary Government
that the Département des Forêts was formed. Their oak trees
have been the foundation of one of Luxembourg's oldest industries, that of tanning, and trees have provided the charcoal
for smelting their iron. During the German invasion their
forests were despoiled and the national riches in timber were
greatly impaired. Reafforestation will, therefore, take an important place in their program of reconstruction.

Denmark is largely a farming country, and only about nine
per cent is regarded as forest. The surface of the country is
uniformly low and flat, and presents little variety; all the same,
it does not give an impression of monotony, because the landscape is enriched by noble forests, green meadows, and fertile
fields. Not long ago the center and west of Jutland were nearly
bare of woods, but in recent years there has been a progressive
planting program. The beech forests are a great feature in
the landscape which they dominate. In the old days oak comprised their main woodlands, but oaks are now comparatively
rare. Pine has been mainly planted on the dunes and sand
wastes. Artificial reproduction is the most general silvicultural
practice, except in the beech forests, which are reproduced
naturally after the preparation of the soil. Acorns are sown to
provide a mixture. The Forestry Association of Denmark consists largely of forest owners, and their forest literature and
works on land reclamation are among the most valuable published in Europe.

The British Isles in the days of the reign of King Canute
of Denmark were still a forest country, for they had not suffered from the invasion of the Romans. But today less than five

per cent of the total area of Great Britain can be classed as forests. Both world wars have ravaged the woodlands, 800,000 acres falling to the ax in World War I, and, before any sort of recovery could be made, a million acres had to be sacrificed to meet the needs of World War II. Following recommendations made by the Forestry Commission, it is proposed to plant five million acres during the next fifty years.

It would not be fitting to conclude this chapter without reference to one of the most striking examples of land reclamation which has taken place in Europe during the past century. The planting of the so-called Landes eastward of the great sand-dune region of Gascony in Southwestern France has now become a classic example to students of forestry in all parts of the world. This area consisted of a territory, triangular in shape, containing two million acres of shifting sands and marshes, on which a few poor shepherds used to eke out a precarious living, getting about as best they could on stilts. In 1837 an engineer of the administration of bridges and roads had the inspiration of improving this section by reafforestation, and at his own expense recovered some 1200 acres in the worst marsh by ditching and planting. His great success encouraged others to follow his example, and in due course the results of the planting became so spectacular that the attention of the government was aroused. A law was passed to enforce planting, and in time 1,750,000 acres were covered with fine forests. They planted the maritime pine and Scots pine. As a result of this land reclamation by reafforestation, the whole countryside has been transformed, and, in place of the poor shepherds, flourishing communities are now to be found.

Perhaps the greatest contribution that French foresters have made to the science of silviculture has been in the sphere of thinning operations. The French were among the first to understand the science of thinning and it was they who put forward advanced theories which in later years became generally accepted.

The major task of the art and science of silviculture is to provide man with indispensable products, to maintain tree

cover on those soils which by reason of their physical characteristics can only be used for forests, and at the same time
assure the advantages of a well-balanced natural economy in
respect of climate and hydrography, without which a lasting
civilization is impossible. It is gradually coming to be univer-
sally recognized that the art and science of forestry can make
the greatest possible contribution to the existence of man on
this planet, for it serves life and provides the essentials to support life. This science deals with the problems of forestry and
forest policy, beginning with the need for the more economic
harvesting of what the forest yields, and extending to vital
questions of the importance of forestry and its adjustment to
the material and spiritual welfare of mankind. It is concerned
with the needs of everyday life in every country, and it is
called to serve every country by pointing the way for practicing
foresters. The experiences of the older countries with sustained-
yield forestry may encourage or warn. They may show the
road to scientific management and prevent the waste of time
and money through falling into proven errors. Nowhere else
on earth is there such a fund of experience in silviculture over
so long a period of time as in Central Europe.

The principles of silviculture are capable of universal application, but it is essential to have a knowledge, in the first place,
of forest ecology, or the science of forest sites, which rests on
soil science and meteorology together with their basic and ac-
cessory disciplines. It is therefore the duty of each country and
state to adapt the general principles to their own particular
needs.

11.

GREEN GOLD OF THE NORTH

Sweden is one of the most wooded countries in the world. The forests cover half the total area of the country and are a primary source of wealth, giving work to hundreds of thousands of those sturdy people who make their livelihood from the trees. This country is of greatest interest to the world at large in forestry matters, because her export of forest products, lumber, wood pulp, and paper is, next to Canada's, the largest in the world, and yet, in spite of that fact, it was only in this century that Sweden became aware of her need for a conservative forest policy.

This country, with 172,876 square miles, occupies the eastern two thirds of the Scandinavian Peninsula. It is not mountainous like Norway, but the greater part consists of low granite hills. It is cut into numerous watersheds, the many rivers furnishing means of transport and providing water power. Little coal is to be found in Sweden, but she is called the kingdom of "white coal"; the "white coal" which has electrified her railroads and brought light and power to her farmers comes as a by-product from the forests. This "white coal" is the power of water. These same waters which bring wealth to the soil pulsate with power, which is harnessed for the use of man. One purpose supplements the other in fulfilling the destiny of the waters as they flow on their way to the sea. The forest is the mother of the rivers and the rivers are the roads of exit and yield the power for industry.

Here is an example of perfectly balanced economy which is brought about by the interplay of the principal natural resources. The forests have delivered the charcoal needed for the refining of ore into the steel for which Sweden is world-famous and the water power has greatly aided the processing of the timber into lumber, pulp, and paper. Formerly many forests were utilized mainly in mining. Before the advent of gunpowder, men used to heat the rock and then cool it rapidly by pouring water over it, the contraction causing the ore-bearing rock to split. In this way enormous quantities of wood were required and great volumes of timber were also converted into charcoal to be used in the blast furnaces for reducing the ore into pig iron. During the seventeenth and eighteenth centuries this part of Sweden provided the world with a considerable portion of its iron and steel, and it was in those days that the foundation was laid for the international reputation of Swedish steel. Present-day mills in Bergslagen still use charcoal in steel making, and "charcoaling" is an important source of employment. The cultivated soil extending into the forest area has molded a hardy population, accustomed to a life in the woods and highly skilled in logging.

The care of the forest has now become the concern of all the Swedish people, in order that the forest yields may be sustained and further improved. The visitor traveling through the southern part of Sweden will find a landscape where fertile farms are interspersed with wooded hills and mountain ranges, the ridges displaying the bare primary rock which serves as the foundation of the entire Scandinavian Peninsula. In this rock will be seen traces left by glaciers which thousands of years ago scooped up the loose earth of the mountain ridges and deposited it in the valleys below. Following the Ice Age, this was submerged by the post-glacial sea, which deposited the layers of clay now constituting the fertile farmland of the country. The Dal River forms the line of demarcation between the two principal forest regions in Sweden, the northern and southern coniferous regions, and at the same time it also forms the northern limit of the oak, *Quercus pedunculata.* In the central part of Sweden proper the forest region begins with pine and spruce, covering the granite hills and plateau, birch and other hardwoods, oak, beech, elm, lime, and poplar being found in the river valleys. The Scots pine, *Pinus silvestris,* and Norway spruce, *Picea excelsa,* are the only indigenous conifers. They are often accompanied by some hardwoods, of which the birches, *Betula berrucosa* and *Betula pubescens,* are the most common. The white stems of the birch trees show up in pleasant contrast to the somber character of the coniferous woods.

Norrland, with the northernmost part called Lapland, is a vast, almost unbroken forest country with a sparse population. Here, too, pine and spruce, with white birch intermixed, are the trees of the country. Towards the northern boundary the white birch increases, and aspen, *Populus tremula,* are frequently found, until finally the treeless tundra appears. A treeless alpine region occupies the northwestern frontier territory, fringed at lower elevations by a belt of birch. This part of Sweden is cut by the Arctic Circle, which is often considered the northern limit for forest growth. But in Sweden the forests continue north of the Arctic Circle because of the proximity of the Gulf Stream. However, where the land rises to any considerable height the influence of the Gulf Stream is not sufficient to provide the necessary temperature for forest vegetation, and the mountains of Lapland are therefore bare of trees.

This great northern forest region remained undisturbed until ninety years ago. Those great stands of pine and spruce had never been touched by man, except in the lower reaches of the rivers; along the valleys were little saw mills. The golden age of the Swedish saw mill industry began when timber tariffs in England and France were lifted. At first these forests suffered grievously, because the plums were taken; the prime timber was removed while the suppressed, dead, and dying trees were left. During the past thirty or forty years, however, public opinion in Sweden has changed all this. Cuttings have been made with due regard to silvicultural principles. Now the overmature and damaged trees are the first to be taken, and trees capable of further growth are retained, while mother seed trees are left to ensure regeneration. Thus the forest capital is maintained to yield its annual wood increment for the wealth of Sweden.

Norway has practically no virgin forest, apart from a few small areas in mountain valleys that have not yet been touched by the ax. Almost all her woodlands are worked economically, with due regard for future yields, and by a new Forest Conservation Act of 1932 all felling is under professional control. The total forest area in Norway is 7,499,033 hectares, or approximately 29,300 square miles. The main species, which grow in her mountainous plateaus and along the sides of her deep valleys and lakes and border her numerous fiords and waterways, are Norway spruce, *Picea abies;* Scots pine, *Pinus silvestris;* birch, aspen, oak, and elm. Fifty-three per cent of the whole forest area is covered by Norway spruce, twenty-eight per cent by Scots pine, while the remaining nineteen per cent consists of hardwoods. Two thirds of the Norwegian woodlands belong to the farmers; this is a fact which is of great importance to economic conditions and which helps to solve the question of employment in the rural districts. Surplus labor readily finds work on the farms in the summer, but the winter months, when the farmlands are frozen, are naturally the busiest times in the woods.

In Norway there are 4,500 sawmills, generally fed by floating rivers. There is, however, plenty of scope for afforestation, because seventy-five per cent of the country is wasteland, while only three per cent of the land is in farms. The most valuable portion, from the forest point of view, is the southeastern corner around Oslo, in eight counties, in which the forest area is as high as fifty per cent, going up to an elevation of 3000 feet. Again, in the three counties around Trondhjem a large and important forest area is located at the head of the fiords.

The entire western coast and the higher elevations are devoid of valuable forest growth, and the northern third of the country, north of the Arctic Circle, is mostly heath and moors, with only seven per cent wooded with inferior birch.

When I way staying at Mandal in South Norway, one evening I was walking along the coast with the late Lord Salvesen, and he pointed out to me a school plantation which had been made by successive generations of scholars. That same evening I went to a dance in the town of Mandal, and mentioned what I had seen to one of my partners, and she explained that each class in the school undertook to plant a given area. She invited me to see the plantation that her class had made when she was a girl at school, fifteen years before. On visiting the forest with my new-found friend, I was interested to see that it consisted of about fifty small compartments ranging from one-year-old to fifty-year-old trees. It was customary for children to take their parents to see the trees of their planting and in many cases the parents themselves could in turn show their children the trees which they had planted in a previous generation.

On a later visit to this hospitable country, I was lecturing before the Royal Norwegian Geographical Society when I met representatives of the Norwegian Forestry Society. They told me that much of the new work of afforestation was being carried out by the Norwegian Army, and that, during maneuvers, the soldiers were largely responsible for fire prevention. It is significant that Norway has treated the question of afforestation with such urgency that it is regarded as a vital part of military preparedness. Here is an example that all the armies of the world might well follow.

Finland, the land of fens and lakes, covers an area of 150,000 square miles, of which half is forest; only Russia and Sweden surpass her in the extent of their forest areas. About two fifths of Finland's woods are owned by the State and are regulated by law. The forests consist principally of spruce and a variety of Scots pine called Riga pine, which is well known for its straight growth and clean bole. Aspen, alder, and birch, especially the latter, are considered forest weeds, and fire is often used to destroy them. Lime, maple, elm, ash, and some oak are to be found, and larch, *Larix Sibirica,* was introduced nearly two centuries ago. The long severe winters and hot dry summers of Finland produce slow growth, the pine in the north requiring 200 to 250 years, or in the middle sections 140 to 160 years, to grow to maturity. This slow growth, forming close annual rings, makes for high quality, and so the timber of Finland is always in great demand.

The Poles are a natural forest people, and it is the greatest ambition of every man to have a piece of land large enough to grow trees on—trees rather than flowers. The best wooded areas of Poland are those in the south and east, and especially in the Carpathians. The total forest area in 1937 was 33,298 square miles, 8,463,000 hectares, or 22.2 per cent; but the woodland area is decreasing in size. During the five years of German occupation two and a half to three times as much forest area was cut yearly as in prewar days. Three quarters of the forests are coniferous, and the remaining quarter deciduous.

Except for the Bialowieza National Park there is little virgin forest in Poland; this area, however, has been protected in its primeval grandeur. In times gone by this forest was the scene of many royal hunting parties famous throughout Europe. This, too, is the last home of the European bison. Even now, after the damage wrought by war, this ancient forest retains its interest and charm for the scientist, forester, artist, and lover of nature. Outstanding among the tree species of Europe is the true silver fir, *Abies alba.* Poland has made two separate reservations for the protection of the last remaining rugged veterans. There is another National Park inside the Czarno-hora, where the mountainsides are covered with a dark mantle of forests, with dwarf pines at high altitudes. Above the spruce region, from 4000 to 5000 feet in altitude, is the realm of dark green mountain pine and juniper. And here may be found dwarf willows, but the tree that towers above the rest is the "limba," or stone pine. These trees grow very slowly and their wood is greatly valued by cabinet-makers, for it is immune to worms. These trees are becoming rare, for only on the slopes of Zabie, near Morskie Oko, and in the Jarorova Valley do forests of them remain.

On the borders of Poland and Czechoslovakia, in the northern foothills of the Tatra Mountains, with all their natural grandeur, is a region of beech and spruce forest with some larch, ash, rowan, and pine. Standing out on many a mountain crag here, too, may be seen silver firs of great age. In autumn they form a fitting background to the dark-red tints of the beech, which contrast with the gold of the larches, forming a magnificent picture. Such gems of beauty may not bring golden gain from lumber, but their aesthetic value is untold, for they speak to the very heart of man.

12.

AMONG THE EVERGREENS

A HUNDRED miles south of Cape Finisterre begins the realm of the evergreen trees and shrubs, which at one time extended from the Atlantic Coast eastwards to the eastern shores of the Black Sea. The peninsulas of the Mediterranean, together with the coastal strip of North Africa, are the natural home of many members of the great family of the evergreens. The people of these territories are much alike in character and temperament and they represent the older civilizations. The Mediterranean shores were once the most populous in the world, but the vast forests which were the very foundation of the well-being of multitudes have disappeared from the mountain ridges, leaving bare rocky spurs and ledges. The humus, accumulated beneath the trees by the decay of leaves and fallen trunks, was washed away. The soil of the alpine pastures which were once surrounded by woods was destroyed. Meadows, too, that were green and fertile became waste and unproductive, because the once tree-surrounded reservoirs that supplied the ancient canals were broken, or the springs that fed them dried up. Rivers famous in history have shrunk to mere brooklets, or have widened into broad expanses of sand and gravel, which are dry in summer, but which in winter are transformed into raging torrents. Sandbars block the entrances of many navigable streams and harbors which once were centers of trade and commerce. Down through the ages their countries have been scarred by war, and in consequence all the accessible forests have grievously suffered. Internal unrest and lack of political stability and long-term policies have hindered the attempts that have been made towards conservation.

Proximity to the sea has enabled these countries to import wood from elsewhere, so that they have not felt the need to adopt farsighted afforestation policies.

In Italy from the earliest times the *legnarii,* or wood merchants, imported their supplies from as far-distant countries as India by way of Alexandria. For ash they went to Asia Minor, for cedar to Cilicia. In Cicero's time there was a regular wood market in Rome, as in Jerusalem, where wood was sold by the pound.

In the past, colonization, exploitation, fire, farming, and goats did away with most of the virgin forests. The plight of these countries might have been even worse, but, fortunately for them, they have largely escaped industrial development and so they have not all seriously felt their forest deficiency, apart from suffering from droughts and floods. Spain is one of the countries that has suffered severely through deforestation. What a wonderful country the whole of the Iberian Peninsula must have been in ancient times, when it was richly clothed with evergreen trees! In the days when Rome was at the height of her power, it was a common saying that in Spain a bird could travel from one end of the country to the other by hopping from tree to tree. According to Diodorus Siculus, the southern provinces were densely wooded until 200 B.C., when the Romans first took possession. But a great forest fire starting from the Pyrenees ran over the country, exposing deposits of silver ore, which invited a large influx of miners and which became the cause of reckless forest destruction. Forests were open to all, and when they were exploited there was no compulsion or inducement to reafforest. Woodland parks such as the paradises of the Persian kings and the *nemora* of the

Romans and Carthaginians were early examples of reserves from which exploiters were excluded. Certain groves were regarded as sacred among the ancients. These were frequent in Greece and Italy, as also in other pagan countries. But even these were violated, as, for example, in Palestine at the time of Joshua's successful campaign, when the Israelites were enjoined to eradicate these groves with ax and fire.

Spain, once a paradise, became almost a desert through neglect, ignorance, indolence, despotism of the Church, and misrule by corrupt bureaucracies. The fertility of much of the land was lost through soil erosion caused by high winds, which gathered force when the evergreen covering of the great forests was removed. Land prepared for tilling became sterile. In the early centuries of the Christian era a prosperous population of 40 millions exploited the country. Then came the dark days of Gothic rule, until a second period of prosperity was enjoyed, at any rate by the sphere influenced by the beneficent rule of the Saracens, who reclaimed deserts and whose irrigation works are the mainstay of agriculture to the present day. Despite centuries of warfare and bloodshed in the effort to establish Christian kingdoms, the country still remained wealthy, when in 1479 the several kingdoms were united under Ferdinand and Isabella. With the discovery of America, yet another era of prosperity was enjoyed by the people, who had then dwindled to 20 millions. But the Inquisition, which also led to the expulsion of the Jews and wholesale emigration to America, undermined the prosperity of the country, and its population had declined to 10 millions by the beginning of the nineteenth century.

Throughout all this time the tree cover suffered and at present the forest is mainly confined to the higher mountains. The most valuable are to be found in the Pyrenees and the Cantabrian Mountains. It has been said that in the past Spain has been noted for its comprehensive legislation without execution, and that official reports were rarely trustworthy. It was not until about 1833 that there was an awakening to the necessity for conservation. It was then that a law was enacted and an ordinance issued at great length, defining the meaning of *montes* and instituting forest inspection.

Some years later a number of young men were sent to the forest school at Tharaud in Germany, and it was probably under the influence of these men on their return, backed by La Sociedad Económica of Madrid, that a commission to formulate a forest law was instituted. In 1846 a school was established at Villaviciosa de Odon, which was later transferred to Escorial, near Madrid. This school, organized on the German lines by Bernardo della Torre Royas, who became its first director, was quite deservedly the pride of Sanish foresters. The creation of a forest department, Cuerpo de Montes, followed, and a general forest survey was made. The forests owned by the State, the communities, and public institutions were divided into three classes according to the species of tree at the time: this appeared to be the easiest way of determining their locations as regards altitude and their public value. These were the coniferous forest, the deciduous oak and chestnut forests, and the forests of ash, alder, and willow, the last-named naturally situated in the lower levels. The first two classes of forest were declared preserves and were strictly protected, while the third class was declared salable. There was an intermediate class composed of cork oak and evergreen oak whose status was left in doubt. Later on, revision of this classification was made. Together with all the forest areas of the first class which were not at least 250 acres in extent, it was added to the salable class. The first class, which was to be reserved, was found to be approximately 17 million acres, of which over a million was owned by the State, while the salable property was found to be about half that area. There followed constant disputes regarding the classification, and repeated attempts were made by different political factions to reduce the forest area. These were opposed by the forest administration, which was forced again and again to reclassify. As the forests became exploited under the Minister of Finance to meet immediate financial needs, the country suffered increasingly from floods and droughts. It so happened that when the sale, in annual installments, of over 4½ million acres was ordered by the Ministry of Finance, the same year there were disastrous floods, causing great loss of life and property, and 28,000 people were made homeless. This was in turn followed by successive droughts. So stirred was the public sentiment that there was a revision of policy which led to the enactment of a reboisement law which ordered the immediate reafforestation of all wasteland in the public forests. Alas, funds were not forthcoming, and by 1895 only 21,000 acres had been reafforested under this law and three quarters of this merely by sowing tree seed.

By the beginning of the twentieth century a new and more promising era was brought about, when the technical administration of the forests was divorced from political influence and brought under the newly created Minister of Agriculture. Popular education was attempted through arbor days, various associations fostering the idea, and in 1904 La Fiesta del Arbol was made a national holiday and prizes were distributed for plantations made on that day. In time this educational campaign bore fruit, and now for over fifty years both government and private enterprise have made every effort to re-create old woodlands.

The plan implemented to bring this about has taken two courses. Directly in charge of this work is the Afforestation Section of the Ministry of Agriculture, headed by experts from the Forestry Corps. Their job is to conserve existing tracts of woodland, to create preserves, and to plant new woods. It is a never-ending task, and one which is catered to in every government budget. Over twenty years ago, in an effort to further and intensify this work, General Primo de Rivera's government set aside a large sum of money. Political changes made it impossible for this financial assistance to be repeated in succeeding years, but in 1942 the Government again made a large appropriation to this end.

Private enterprise, inspired by the good financial prospects offered by the timber industry at the end of World War I, has also carried out some important afforestation programs, which have been mainly concentrated in the north of Spain, where the climate is particularly suitable for this kind of cultivation.

Public interest in the Government's efforts has been aroused, in the first place, by the teachers in rural schools, who have made every effort to kill the centuries-old country prejudice against trees and imbue their pupils with a "tree-consciousness." This has been helped by the introduction of a "Tree Day," on which each child throughout the country plants his own little tree, to be tended and looked after by him during his playtime and vacations.

Propaganda and the vigilance of forest keepers have also helped to consolidate the State's authority and avoid wholesale tree felling. At the same time, official undertakings have, where possible, given every help to firms interested in afforestation, but, because of lack of financial means, the results have not always been up to the measure of their hopes.

Portugal is the country of pine and cork oak. This small country, which occupies the west coast of the Iberian Peninsula, with 36,000 square miles and 6 million people, is fortunate in having a larger proportion of fertile land than her larger neighbor. The northern section is mainly mountainous and has extensive sand dunes, large areas of which have been reclaimed by tree planting. The central part is hilly and not so well wooded, although it contains some of the best-managed forests. In Estremadura, planted pines cover an area of 25,000 acres. The southern area, of semitropical climate and flora, is rich in farmlands and has extensive cork-oak plantations.

The entire forest area of the country, including brushwood and scrub forest, is perhaps under a million acres. Eighty per cent is coniferous, consisting of *Pinus pinaster* and *Pinus pinea*. The remaining twenty per cent is cork oak and other oaks mixed with Spanish or sweet chestnut, *Castanea sativa*. Cork from the bark of the cork oak is the principal export, and the pines are tapped for turpentine and resin, which are exported as naval stores.

Portugal's first attempt at the scientific management of her forests was made in the middle of the nineteenth century. However, a regular organization was not established until later, under a Director General of Commerce and Industries. At the beginning of the twentieth century a more thorough organization of reafforestation was made, and allowed Government expropriations of wastelands in the interest of the public. The School of Agriculture in Lisbon is responsible for the education of the technical forestry staff.

The pine forests, whether natural or planted, possess a charm of their own. They have been described with great feeling by Evelyn Harbord, Schools' Secretary of The Men of the Trees, who knew them so well in prewar days. She tells how they grow on the undulating plateau between two ranges of great mountains and, sloping southwards, end at the feet of the highest mountain of the country, Sierra da Estrela, the Mountain of the Star. It is this undulation that gives the forests their charm, the waving, mingling lines of many horizons, fading, dipping, rising like waves of a rough sea. In early morning the mists cling to the treetops, pale and paler in the distance, and at sunset they look pink and soft as clouds. In such woods there are few birds, though in the clearings the nightingales sing loudly both by day and by night and sometimes a pair of golden orioles will flash amid the green. But the thickest parts of the forest are silent and still. Nothing disturbs the quiet except, perhaps, an old woodman trimming the trees or changing the earthenware pots on their trunks, which are put there to catch the turpentine. He loves his trees, and seems to belong to the forest and share its rhythm.

Forest destruction in every country spells disaster in one form or another. Whereas, for instance, in Africa it brings erosion and deserts and in Switzerland avalanches, in Italy the rivers are turned into torrents and floods by deforestation. In Italy, therefore, it was the urgent need of protecting their watersheds that induced efforts to secure economic forest management. But the enforcement of wise forestry laws involved national sacrifice, and so in the past it was found difficult to introduce any reform, and many a time when attempts were made to enforce protective measures serious trouble arose.

With her dense population of over 40 millions on 119,000 square miles, with over one third of the country unproductive or unused and a large proportion of this incapable of being reclaimed, no country offers better opportunities for studying the disastrous effect of deforestation on soil and waterflow. The geology, topography, and climate are such that, once the forest cover is removed, disaster is certain. Slates and limestones on steep hills and mountainsides, when bared of trees and pastured by millions of goats, produce ideal conditions for bringing about the flooding of rivers. The melting snow and the heavy spring rains turn them into raging torrents.

About a quarter of Italy's forests are found in the Alps, and a further half are situated on either side of the Apennines, the backbone of this peninsula. Less than a third of her trees and woodlands are distributed over the mainland, while the balance is found on the islands. Sicily was once magnificently wooded, though it is now largely denuded, and Sardinia is still one of the best-wooded parts of Italy. High up in the Alps are the birch, spruce, fir, larch, and pine, and here and there in remote, unexploited spots in the tops of the Apennines a similar cover may still be found, although for the greater part these slopes are occupied by inferior brush forest, coppice, or open forest with scattered trees among rough scrub and thorns. Although there are few forests of any value in Italy, the country is by no means treeless, for poplar, ash, and elm are dotted over the plains and slopes, where they are often planted for vine supports and to mark boundaries. These trees are frequently mutilated by pollarding in a country where firewood is a scarce commodity. Olive plantations and chestnut groves cover 2 million acres of the lower slopes. Eight million acres in vineyards, with their living vine supports, add to the wooded appearance of the country and provide firewood and charcoal for domestic and industrial purposes. Along the sand dunes and near the seashore may be found the maritime and

Aleppo pine and the umbrella-shaped *Pinus pinea*. Here, too, are the picturesquely erect Roman cypresses, which are seen in groups or small groves, while above, in a region up to 1200 feet above sea level, are olives, cork oak, and evergreen oak. Osiers are grown for basketmaking, while on the mountain-sides may be found forests of Scots pine, *Pinus silvestris* and *Pinus laricio,* with a large proportion of fir, *Abies pectinata*. Much of the hardwood forest is managed as coppice for the manufacture of charcoal.

In Southern Italy the vegetation takes on a tropical appearance, with its date-palm, orange, lemon, and citron trees. The evergreen effect is intensified by the foliage of the laurels, myrtles, and oleanders, with forests of arbutus, or strawberry trees, and the evergreen oak.

For centuries, from the fall of the Roman Empire until the end of the eighteenth century, Italy has been the victim of war and strife with neighboring countries, and, within her borders, has struggled vainly with the inevitable legacy of denuded lands. However, during the nineteenth century many efforts were made to introduce conservation laws. The devastating floods of 1882 led to much agitation for reboisement; but although laws were passed, they rarely received effective application. Yet the forest department persistently tried to promote reafforestation by giving prizes and distributing millions of young trees and quantities of seed from its nurseries and by furnishing free advice to planters.

It is interesting to note that Italy was the first country to celebrate the armistice after World War I by tree planting. On that day the inhabitants of many a mountain village gathered to pay tribute to those whom they had loved and lost by planting trees in their names.

To two Italians is due the credit for having found that the true reason for the salubrity of forest air is the absence of pathogenic bacteria. It is also to the renown of Italy that she was one of the first to recognize by legislation the forest influence on health conditions. The belief that deforestation of the marshy lowlands between Pisa and Naples produced ma-

larial fever led the Trappist monks of the cloister at the Tre
Fontane to make plantations of eucalyptus. But one of the
greatest things Italy ever achieved in the forestry world was to
convene the first World Forestry Congress, which was held at
the International Bureau of Agriculture in Rome in 1926 and
was attended by representative foresters from almost every
country in the world. This congress had its inception at my
camp in the Highlands of Kenya, when Dr. Caviccioni, the
Italian representative for East Africa, lunched with me and
witnessed a march-past of the first Watu wa Miti (Men of the
Trees). He had been impressed by the way in which warring
tribesmen had responded to an appeal and banded themselves
together to protect their vanishing forests and to plant trees
in their old farms to safeguard the forests of the future and the
fertility of their lands. As, clan by clan, they passed before
him, my Italian visitor became more and more enthused and
excited. On my return to Europe I contacted a number of
young men in Genoa and was able to interest them in the
importance of my subject. They lost no time in getting to
work, and the outcome was that three years later the World
Forestry Congress took place in Rome.

As one of the delegates to this congress, I had the opportunity of meeting the representatives from all parts of the
world. The usual procedure was to listen to each other's papers
being read in the mornings and to devote the afternoons to
expeditions into the Italian forests. Never before had the Italian Forestry Service had such a splendid opportunity of ex-
changing views and gaining the expert advice of admitted
masters in the art and science of forestry. The visitors, for their
part, were interested to see what had been done by way of
planting, sometimes under the most adverse conditions. One
of the expeditions took us to Vallombrosa, where the first
Institute Forestale had been founded in 1869. There we saw
mountainsides which had once been bared of their forest
growth and all their humus, but which were now reclothed
with great firs. We were told how monks used to chip holes in
the sides of precipitous rocks, then fetch earth in bags from

Sweden Understands the Importance of Wind-screening by Trees

The Judean Hills, Which Will Soon Again be Clothed in Jerusalem
Pines and Cypress

There is No Country in the World That Would Show Greater Response to Planting—The Harbor at Haifa

Reclothing Bare and Desiccated Hill Tracks—A Shelter-wood Regeneration Area

Dawn in the Pacific

Baobab Tree, North
western Australia

Ruthless Destruction of the Forest Began—Felling a Big Tree in the Karri Forests of Western Australia

On the next two pages: A Himalayan Forest

This King of Forest Trees—Kauri Pine, North Auckland, New
Zealand

The Dignity of the Mighty Forests—Road Cut through Virgin Forest, South Island, New Zealand

The Silence of a Hundred Centuries—Puraroto Caves, North Island, New Zealand

the valleys below, and into each pocket of soft humus tuck a tiny seedling until the mountainside was once again fixed and enjoying the green mantle of the firs. The name of this mountain village, once again tree-surrounded, brings to mind Milton's "Leaves . . . In Vallombrosa," which may have referred to the sturdy beech trees that fix the soil of the mountain top above the firs planted by thoughtful brothers in bygone centuries.

At that congress the forestry representatives from every country pooled their sources of information and came to the conclusion that the world was heading for a timber famine which would be experienced within forty years. My subsequent world tour led me to regard this as a very conservative estimate, and the devastating effects of World War II may precipitate this foretold famine sooner than anticipated.

Greece was another country which in times gone by was richly clothed with evergreens. Originally the whole of this peninsula, with a few small exceptions, was a continuous forest. Under the régime of the ancient Greeks the forests were protected by thousands of woodland deities and nymphs of the holy groves, until the fanaticism of the early Christians led to a war against these pagan strongholds, in which the holy groves were destroyed by ax and fire. Centuries of misrule, overtaxation, reckless cutting, and extensive herding of goats and sheep, together with fires, have reduced the forest area until today it covers but 1,917,980 hectares, or 15.1 per cent, of the whole area of that country. Indeed, there is no virgin forest left. The many islands are entirely deforested and so are the seashores—where in olden times dense shady poplars stood —leaving a scene of barren sand and dreary rock.

The forest in northern and middle Greece is confined to the two mountain ranges which run parallel north and south with Mount Olympus and Mount Pindus as the highest elevations. The large plains of Thessaly and Boeotia are treeless; so is the large Arcadian plateau of the Peloponnesos; so, too, are the other smaller but fertile plains and plateaus. The most valuable conifer forest is found in the higher ranges, between 2500 and 5000 feet, below the snow-clad mountain tops, where especially two species of fir, *Abies Apollinis* and *Abies reginae Amaliae,* with other firs and several species of juniper and cypress, form extensive forests. Other common trees are chestnut, sycamore, several species of oak, poplar, and, on the coast, *Pinus halepensis.* The firs occupy about one third of the forest area, evergreen oaks and other evergreen trees another third, while the remaining area is deciduous.

The climate is favorable to tree growth and the soil would readily reclothe itself if left alone. The winters are short, with hardly any ice or snow, except on the high mountains, and trees will grow for nine months in the year. The temperature ranges from 20° to 160° F., the rainfall averages 400 millimeters, and, although the summers are rainless and dry, the other seasons are humid, and rapid growth results from these conditions. But the continued pasturing of millions of goats and sheep prevents any natural regeneration. The practice of permitting people to collect dry wood for fuel leads to forest fires, and perhaps nowhere are forest fires more frequent, in spite of heavy penalties. The forest destruction has had baneful influence on the water condition and river flow, and in no other country is a tree sense more badly needed.

During the enemy occupation of World War II the forests of Greece suffered great ravages. The destruction was effected on the one hand by over-felling carried out directly by the enemy to the extent of denuding certain forest areas, and, on the other, by the disintegration of the Hellenic organization and management. The great ravages were near cities or inhabited areas on bordering road or railway arteries. Further forest areas were sacrificed to accommodate thousands of refugees from Asia Minor, Thrace, and Russia after the Asia Minor disaster.

The great tragedy of Greece is that little is being done to restore her forests. It is the exception rather than the rule to find planters of trees amongst the people, although some forestry operations are carried out by officials of the State.

To many of the Balkan States their forests are a symbol of liberty: in Yugoslavia, for instance, the forests are not only an important factor in the national economy, but also a cherished motif in her national poetry. How great is the love of her people for the forest is shown by the fact that one of the most important Yugoslav provinces was named Sumadija, derived from the word *suma,* forest. Dr. Ljubo Leontič, Yugoslav Ambassador to the Court of St. James, addressing delegates to the World Forestry Charter Luncheon held in London in 1946, said that it was there in Sumadija that the flag of the national movement for liberation was first unfurled 140 years ago and where the liberation movement of World War II began and whence it spread all over the country. He said: "It is not astonishing, therefore, that my people have looked to the forests as a stronghold of their liberty." That was why invaders would always start by cutting down the forests before attacking the people, in the hope that by so doing they would destroy the resistant forces.

For many years Rumania has been developing her forestry systems over her 48,000 square miles, half of which are hilly and mountainous, and the remainder the rich, alluvial valley of the Danube. This latter is now largely deforested. The hill and mountain country was, until the eighteenth century, well wooded, but then it was sorely depleted to meet the demands of Turkish markets. The wars of this century have naturally made further inroads and it has been estimated that but ten per cent of the total area of the country remains forest.

Bulgaria, with its 38,000 square miles, is fortunate in possessing extensive forests, which comprise one third of the total land area. Although Bulgaria touches the zone of the evergreens, much of its forests consist of oak, beech, and walnut. In the past, waste, neglect, and mining requirements had stripped the country of many of the dense forests with which it was once covered. However, the more inaccessible woodlands still flourish in the north up to altitudes of over 2600 feet; these are mainly of beech and oak, while many of the southern mountains are clad with conifers to well over 3000

feet. Bulgaria is a fertile country and with the introduction of
more conservative measures might well maintain a much
greater population.

Hungary has a total area of approximately 707,000 hectares
containing the following species: oak, beech, hornbeam, acacia,
ash, elm, poplar, willow, Scotch fir, black pine, and other firs.
They have an active Forestry Department under the Minister
of Agriculture, which takes care of regeneration. Forestry reserves are needed for her requirements, and some timber for
building is imported from Rumania.

Following the realm of the evergreens, we come to Turkey,
famous for her great number of species of forest trees. She has
no fewer than eleven different kinds of oak, including evergreen oak and the well-known Turkey oak. Here, too, are the
chestnut-leaved oak, which in the East provides food for the
silkworms producing shantung. There are five maples, four
pines, four true firs, and six junipers, which strike an evergreen note wherever grown. These and many other forest trees
cover a total area of 10,500,000 hectares, 300,000 hectares of
which represents virgin forest.

Although in the past the forests of the Ottoman Empire
have suffered under misrule, in more recent times an effort has
been made to work the forests on a sustained-yield basis. Two
methods are now used for regeneration: natural regeneration
and planting. Cleared spaces of the forest are regenerated
through the process of natural regeneration, while the planting is used to develop green belts around villages which have
no forests of their own. This latter planting started in 1934,
and in that year 52 hectares were planted; in 1944, 1157 hectares, and in 1945, 1438 hectares; and so it may be seen that a
steady planting program is in progress. Natural regeneration
was started in 1945, and in the following two years an area of
100 hectares was regenerated. Great credit is due to those who
have inspired this recent forestry development.

Palestine has been described as a bridge between Asia and
Africa, but this actually applies only to the maritime plain.
This was the great route followed by many an invading army,
as well as by trade and commerce throughout the centuries.

From Egypt it enters Palestine at Gaza and goes northwards to the Plain of Esdraelon by way of one of the famous passes, either Megiddo or Dothan. In ancient times practically the whole of the country was well wooded and until this day it has retained its name, Palestine, although the Philistines disappeared considerably over 2000 years ago. The Philistines were a natural forest people, and their land was well described as the Land of Promise. Their wooded hills guarded fertile valleys, and the presence of sacred groves at the source of mountain springs is evidence that they had a natural regard for trees. Even in the days of the Jewish prophets, the country must have been well wooded, for were there not "lurking places for she-bears" which would come out and devour unruly children who were disrespectful?

In Byzantine days the country supported a population of about 3 million, and today Zionist authorities have estimated that the land might be made to provide homes for 2 to 4 millions above present population. The key to future prosperity lies in large-scale reafforestation; until the hills are once again reclothed, the valleys will not regain their former fertility. This fact is now generally recognized, and even under the rigors of World War I, Allenby initiated a planting campaign. This was further developed by The Men of the Trees in 1929, when many nurseries were started for the raising of young trees, and Arabs and Jews worked happily side by side to reclaim the land. An educational campaign was started through arbor days, and the Feast of the Trees became a nationwide day of tree planting. There is no national conflict in planting, and many of the Jewish settlements have done splendid work. Malarial marshes have been planted with eucalyptus, or reclaimed for agriculture and citrus groves. Still more ambitious projects are planned for reclaiming areas of the Negeb. Some years ago, while visiting the Holy Land, I suggested that a canal be cut from Haifa to Tiberias, a very short distance as the crow flies. This would flood the Jordan Valley and, with some further excavations at the southern end, provide an inland water route to the Red Sea, Africa, and India. The cutting of this canal would increase precipitation along its route and assist the much-needed planting throughout the region. Now the latest suggestion is that a Jordan Valley Authority be set up to use the sweet waters of the Jordan to irrigate the belt of land on the west bank of this river and create a system of terraces on the steep slopes and at the same time to use the fall of the water to create cheap electric power. It is proposed that a portion of the Jordan should be carried westward in a tunnel to fertilize the Plain of Esdraelon. It has been pointed out that this would interfere with the water supply of the Dead Sea and so, to make up this loss, the salt water of the Mediterranean may be let in, and this fall of the water used to generate still more power. Whichever project is adopted, large-scale planting should follow. The Men of the Trees have led the way and have done much to educate public opinion as to forestry needs, but much remains to be done. Each year at least 12,000 acres should be planted with 12 million trees. I estimate that the whole of Palestine might be reafforested at the cost of a single day of war. There is no country in the world that needs trees so urgently, or would show greater response to planting than this land of promise.

One of the best-known trees of the North African evergreen belt is the Atlas Mountain cedar, *Cedrus atlantica*, and, in fact, the greatest distinction of the North African mountains is still the cedars, though few but battered veterans now remain where once great forests stood. Their enemies have been man, goats, and erosion. Along the seashore the tamarisk fixes the sand and often provides the first shelter; casuarinas, too, pinelike in appearance, add to the evergreen effect. Palms there are in plenty, and olive groves have their place in the foothills. But by far the best-known cedar is that which grows in Lebanon, and these were made forever famous by the Hebrew poet when he wrote:

> The trees of the Lord are full of sap;
> The cedars of Lebanon, which He has planted;
> Where the birds make their nests.

This beautiful tree is chiefly associated in our minds with lawns and parks, though it may become a valuable timber tree when grown silviculturally. After all, it was probably from this wood that King Solomon built his temple. When excavating ancient cities with Sir Flinders Petrie in South Palestine, I was able to identify charred beams as cedar. The only indigenous forest of *Cedrus libani* is that of Lebanon, where about 400 trees still stand. In spite of ravages by goats and the demand for wood, these few veterans have survived the ages. Surely these historic trees should be protected and reinforced by further planting and become a place of pilgrimage.

Cyprus is famous for another cedar cousin, *Cedrus brevifolia,* which was discovered in the mountains by Sir Samuel Baker in 1879, growing at an altitude of 4300 feet. The only other true cedar, *Cedrus Deodara,* is indigenous to the Himalayan Mountains.

Although the borders of the Mediterranean are the home of many of the evergreens, the trees readily adapt themselves to a great variety of climates and would welcome the hospitality of other countries.

13.

THE WEALTH OF INDIA

To REACH India from the evergreen belt, one must traverse deserts and waterless wastes. These countries cradled civilization when their hills and plains were green with trees. The deserts of Iran and Mesopotamia tell the same story, first of gradual soil exhaustion and then of more rapid erosion. The mighty empires of Babylon, Syria, Persia, and Carthage were destroyed by the advance of floods and deserts caused by the clearing of forests for agricultural land and by having their rivers drawn upon for additional supplies of water for irrigation. Their pristine fertility simply ran down under agriculture, worn out after long use. The ancient irrigation systems of Iraq have long been in decay and the water-holding forests which fed their streams met the same fate as others in remote antiquity.

The traveler from the Mediterranean will encounter the great Iranian range known to the ancients as the Zagros. These mountains sweep from the Caucasus in an almost unbroken curve, following roughly the line of the Turkish frontier and the Persian Gulf, until they fade away in the barren plains on the Baluchistan frontier, a distance of over 1400 miles. Only here and there are wooded slopes, remnants of the ancient tree covering, but for the greater part the mountain scenery is bare and rugged, with gray outcrops of slate forming part of a tangled mass of rock. Every kind of geological formation appears, as if thrown up by some cosmic upheaval. Permanent vegetation is rare, and in the rainless summer the rocks are hot and lifeless until they respond to the first rains in November by showing a faint green film, which by the spring has become a mass of luxuriant grass dotted with scarlet poppies and many other brightly colored flowers. By April the flora is scorched by the sun and by May the rocks are once again bare. In July the temperature rises to the burning heat of 120°. When the forests of Iran are restored, the country will once again become a paradise on earth.

Even though much of Iran is desert, some parts have retained their beauty and fertility. There are still great valleys between the various ranges of the Kerman Mountains, which abound with the most rare and valuable forest products. Parts of the provinces of Fars, Khuzistan, Ardeman, and Azerbaijan are rich with luxuriant vegetation, and the provinces of Gilan and Mazanderan, which lie between the Elburz and the Caspian Sea, enjoy woodland and water scenery. The mountainsides are clothed with trees and shrubs, while the plain, 300 miles long and from five to thirty miles wide, is dotted with mulberry plantations, vineyards, orchards, and orange groves.

Much mountainous country guards the western gate of India.

Forest exploitation has been responsible for much of the catastrophic erosion that scars the foothills of the Himalayas, and the human population of India, which is increasing at the rate of about 3 millions a year, makes ever further inroads upon India's forest wealth. The primeval forests, which once covered the country, are making their last stand in the hills and mountain systems. Even so, many of the hills have been deforested by reckless destruction during many generations, with the result that the climate and the water supply, upon which the very life of man depends, have deteriorated until desert conditions are met with in many an erstwhile fertile area. It was not until quite late under British rule that conservation of India's forest wealth was contemplated. The British, like other nations, gained a foothold in India for trading purposes during the seventeenth century, but not before the middle of the nineteenth century did the forests come under administration. The name of B. H. Baden-Powell, at one time Conservator of the Punjab and acting Inspector-General of Forests during 1872–1874, is closely connected with placing forest conservation on a sound basis, although as far back as 1856 a German forester from Hesse, Dietrich Brandis, was installed as Superintendent of Forests for Pegu, with wide powers, and was later entrusted with the organization of forest conservancy, with the result that today India is one of the bright exceptions to the indifference and neglect of forestry matters within the British Commonwealth.

The Indias, including Hindustan, Pakistan, Afghanistan, Burma, and Ceylon, with a total land area of 2,186,500 square miles and a population of 427,000,000, possess a forest area of 486,304 square miles, or 22.2 per cent of the total land area. The Indian Empire contains every kind of elevation, climate, aspect, and soil, and its forests are among the richest and most varied in the world. This region contains at least 2500 different species of trees. The old "British India," including Burma, comprises more than sixty per cent of the whole, the remainder being under the rule of the Indian States. In British territory the Government forests occupied an area of 251,572 square miles. These forests first became famous for teak and other valuable woods, which were exploited without thought for the future until the Indian Forest Service was brought into being. This Forest Service has now admittedly become one of the finest in the world and has provided a model for other countries both within and without the British Commonwealth.

One of the first measures of the administration was to demarcate forest reserves. Suitable forest laws and codes had to be published for each area. Agreements were drawn up with the owners of the land, and under these settlements the lands were legally constituted as Government Forest Reserves. All questions relating to the customs, rights, and privileges of inhabitants had to be decided with due consideration. As soon as the forest reserves are properly constituted, silvicultural systems are introduced with a view to working them on a sustained-yield basis. Throughout the whole of once-British India, all forests capable of management today have their working plans, which are carried out as efficiently as in any forests in the world. Mr. D. Bourke-Borrowes, late of the Indian Forestry Service, recently described the great progress that had been made in India during the past century. The areas covered by plantations and afforestation now amount to several hundreds of thousand acres. The achievements accomplished in the work of reafforestation and land reclamation afford examples of great variety and magnitude. One of the early projects was started as far back as 1866, when the irrigated plantations in the Punjab were formed to provide an adequate supply of timber and fuel for the inhabitants of the bare plains. These plantations now comprise an area of about 60,000 acres. Where the forests had suffered from excessive grazing, producing widespread erosion, land reclamation and afforestation have been systematically carried out for many years past. One of the methods employed is to erect earthen dams across the ravines and sow the areas immediately behind such dams with suitable crops of trees. Much of the reclamation work in Central and Western India has consisted of reclothing bare and desiccated hill tracts situated in localities with very small rainfall. Such work is a slow and arduous undertaking.

It has been found by experience that where the indigenous vegetation can be maintained indefinitely, and at the same time be utilized economically, the problem of soil conservation ceases to exist. This is the aim of the Indian Forestry Service, and the object of sustained-yield forestry and controlled grazing. This system consists of managing a forest so that only as much wood is cut every season as is contained in the trees that would have died in the natural course of events, or where more is cut, the indigenous tree growth is correspondingly stimulated or reinforced by planting. Controlled grazing sees to it that the floral composition of the pastures does not materially change or, at any rate, does not deteriorate. Many of the methods to reclaim eroded land come within the scope of agriculture, where contour farming has proved to be advantageous in many cases. Shifting cultivation and uncontrolled clearing and burning are contributing factors to the enormous reduction of forest acreage.

The greatest forest-tree region is that of the western Himalayan Mountains, from the Indus to the Sardah River on the Nepal frontier. This is the realm of great conifers, outstanding among which is the Himalayan cedar, *Cedrus Deodara,* which thrives from 4000 to 10,000 feet up, growing gregariously in association with spruce, blue pine, and three different kinds of oak. Sometimes the silver fir joins in with cypress, while yew is often found growing under its shade. At low elevations the deodar mixes with the long-leaved pine. Among other trees to be found in the cedar forests are the birch, poplar, horse chestnut, elm, hazel, hornbeam, maple, bird-cherry, walnut, holly, box, and rhododendron, the latter sometimes growing to almost tree height. The leaf fall of these nurse trees provides rich humus for the cedars.

What do we know of the secret life of these magnificent cedars which dominate the great mountain range from which they have taken their name? How do they manage to reproduce their kind and reign as princes in their forest paradise? How have they come to rule the heights? Millions of years ago they covered large tracts of the earth's surface, as may be proved by examining the fossilized remains gathered by geologists from the debris of their diggings. It is impossible to tell the difference between the deodar and its cousin from the mountains of Lebanon, or, indeed, from its other cousin, which prefers the Atlas Mountains. The wood at the heart of these trees looks the same and to all intents and purposes is the same. These cousins differ only in form and foliage. In time of flood they each migrated to the hills, where they survived by adapting themselves to the conditions with which they had to contend. The cedar of Lebanon and that of the Atlas Mountains had to protect themselves against drying winds, and for that reason they developed smaller leaves, so that they should not transpire too much moisture. The Himalayan cedar had to contend with the snows, and so he cunningly developed a drooping character with longer leaves, which enabled him to shed the snows without the risk of limb break. The male and female flowers of the deodar are generally found on separate individuals, but this is not always so, and monoecious trees are often met with by those who have carefully watched the business of pollinization. In October, at the end of the rainy season, the young female cones expectantly open their scales, which, when pollinated, close again. The cones hide their secret through the following winter, when they increase but little in size, but with the coming of spring growth becomes fast. By the following October the cones are mature, and in November they break up, discharging winged seeds, some of which may find root in the weeds or moss of the forest floor.

Good seed years come irregularly, perhaps every three or four years. On the fringe of the forest, where the blue pine grows with the deodar, the young growth of both comes on together; but the blue pine grows faster, and may swamp the slower-growing deodar. The blue pine, *Pinus excelsa,* has from five to eight needles in a cluster and cylindrical, soft-scaled cones. It looks like the Weymouth pine, but has much longer leaves and larger cones, and its bark, which is grayish-brown, is cut by shallow fissures into small, rather irregular plates. The flowers appear in the spring, and the cones ripen during the following autumn.

Lower down in the same mountain range are cedralas, deciduous trees which grow at heights of up to 4000 feet in the Punjab and eastwards, chiefly along streams. They are handsome trees with light, feathery foliage, and are rapid in growth. Their wood is durable and not eaten by white ants. It has a pleasing scent, and, in fact, is well known as the cigar-box cedar. Celtis is also found in these forests, and is planted around villages, where it is lopped for cattle fodder. The wood is tough and used for oars, tool handles, walking-sticks, and wherever elasticity is required. Albizzia is another large deciduous tree. Siris is one of the best-known Indian trees, for it is not only very common in forests almost all over the country, but is cultivated in avenues and gardens. It is one of the fastest-growing trees, with beautiful, sweet-scented flowers. In contrast, *Olea,* the family of olives, is a slower-growing, yet useful hill tree, chiefly found near villages and in valleys, partly in forests and partly on the borders of fields. It is prized by the villagers, and rarely cut down—though regularly lopped, so that it often has a rounded crown. The wood is valued for turning, for combs, agricultural implements, and fuel. In this region palms are scarce, but canes and wild dates are sometimes to be found. The more valuable of these forests are worked for the supply of Indian railways, while the wood of the pines is floated downstream to be used for building in the plains.

The chief trees of the dry region of the Punjab, Rajputana, Sind, and Baluchistan are species of acacia, prosopis, capparis, salvadora, tamarisk, and *Populus euphratica;* these are the *rukhs* of the Punjab. The most important species in the forests of Baluchistan are *Juniperus macropoda, Pistacia,* and *Olea.* All these forests are worked to supply country needs.

The plains and sub-Himalayan tract of the northwestern provinces, known as the United Provinces, are characterized by the presence of sal, *Shorea robusta,* a gregarious tree of great importance, which is found mixed with species of terminalia, lagerströmia, bombax, careya, schleichera, adina, eugenia, figs, and many others. The soil in which they grow is sandy gravel. Where the soil is deep and moist, sal disappears, and the mixed forest which takes its place includes albizzia, acacia, and dalbergia. Here, too, is one of the world's most delicately scented woods, sissu, which is much sought after for making family chests.

Another important forest region lies in Central India, and includes the country lying south of the Jumna and north of the Godavery River, the Vindhia and Satpura Hills, as well as Orissa and the Circars on the east, and Khandesh and Guzerat on the west. This is the great deciduous, dry forest of India, which extends over the whole of the region, and passes northwards into that previously described. All this region is also chiefly worked for country supply, except for teak and sal, used on the railways. In the western part, teak is the chief tree, while sal dominates the eastern part. There are many other genera and some bamboos. In ravines, palms and tree ferns are sometimes found growing with wild mango.

The eastern Himalaya is a vast region with a great variety of forest trees. In the higher slopes are many firs, spruce, larch, yew, juniper, and hemlock spruce. These range downwards until they reach the zone of the rhododendrons, which are mixed with oaks and chestnuts, while lower still are great maples, magnolias, and other less-known species. Still farther down appear large trees of cedrela, terminalia, with palms and large screw-pines, *Pandanus furcatus,* and these once again pass into sal forests, with the addition of *Schima Wallichii* and *Dillenia.*

The forests of the Khasia Hills are well known for their many species of oak. Passing southwards from Northern Bengal, the Assam Valley, and the Khasia Hills, is a great forest region which extends from the Valley of Cachar southwards down the Lushai Hills to the border of Arrakan and eastwards to the boundaries of Burma. In this great forest are giant trees on deep, rich alluvial lands and along rivers and smaller growth with dense masses of bamboo on the hills. In the Chittagong Forest are the dipterocarpus trees. They are truly magnificent, towering to a height of 150 to 200 feet, mounting over the other forest denizens, which themselves form a second tier but a little way below their superiors. The wealth of this tree is exploited by the villagers, who tap it for its oil. A single tree may yield as much as 7 pounds of oil each night. This is sought after for making torches, and that amount would be sufficient to make a hundred torches, or to paint a small house or a boat. It is at night that the Indian goes into the forest to collect this treasured oil. He makes a hole at breast height, or about 4 feet above the root of the tree, and in it lights a few dried leaves every third evening. The wood of this great tree is used in house building and for dugout canoes; logs from 40 to 60 feet in length are often dragged out of the forest.

There are two other forest regions, that of the southern part of the Deccan Plateau, the slopes of the plateau on the east and south, and the Carnatic Country. These forests are deciduous, but with more teak than is found elsewhere, and sal disappears. Among the species particularly noted are the sandal tree, which will grow on half-bare, stony forest lands. Here, too, are ebony and satinwood. In this region are large tracts covered with the Palmyra Palm, one of the most useful of Indian plants, for its strong, tough outside wood is valuable in house building, and its leaves and fruit provide valuable products.

In the last region come the forests of the mountain range of the Western Ghats with the lands between their foothills and the sea. In some places there are dry areas with growth not unlike that of the deciduous forest of Central India, with a good deal of teak, though the greater part consists of hill forests on lower hill slopes, evergreen in character, and here teak is the dominant tree.

Burma is the main home of this world-famous timber tree, *Tectona grandis,* as it is called. For a century or more the wealth of its forests has been exploited by governments and concessionaires. The trees are girdled while still standing; thus they are killed and partly seasoned before they are laid low. When they fall to earth they often bring with them a shower of debris and creepers by which they had been attached to their neighbors. Next they are cross-cut into logs of convenient length. Teams of elephants are used to extract them from their jungle home. Great is the sagacity of the Burmese elephant, who will guide the log along a difficult trail and eventually bring it to the desired destination. It is fascinating to watch a big elephant pick up a log, carefully balancing it on his tusks and maneuvering it between the tall stems of standing trees. The large logs are dragged to the nearest floating river and pushed over its bank. On striking the water, they are carried downstream to the rafting point. As they pass into the main current, skilled Burmese loggers spring from the bank and ride the logs to their destined place, to form the huge raft in which they will find their way down the great river to the sea.

Modern man is making increasing demands on the wealth of these mighty forests—these forests which contain a greater variety of trees than any others in the world. There is abundance for all, if they are wisely exploited and worked on a sustained-yield basis.

14.

THE TRAGEDY OF CHINA

THE GOOD EARTH from which man sprang, the gentle mother that bore him from her womb, must be tended with loving care; otherwise she will not support him. The body of Earth must have her green covering of trees or other plants. Her skin is sensitive to the behavior of man, who has never quite mastered the art of continuous cultivation of land which was once covered with forest. The folly of exposing her nakedness has been shown graphically in China. Deserts now reign in the very birthplace of ancient civilization. The great northwest loessial region now resembles a huge battlefield, scarred and denuded. That fertile soil which when touched by rain will bear crops two or three times a year easily dissipates itself unless covered by trees or grasses.

The name "loess" is adopted from that of a Tertiary deposit which appears in the Rhine Valley. It is a brownish-colored earth, extremely porous, it crumbles easily between the fingers, and it readily forms clouds of dust. The wind-blown loess is one of the richest soil materials known and its qualities are similar to that which has formed the black soils of the Russian steppes. In the Province of Shansi, loess often covers the subsoil to a great depth and is extremely sensitive to erosion, which will cut it into deep clefts, making traveling across its surface impossible. Over vast areas, where once the soil was deep and fertile, little remains but gaping chasms, sometimes hundreds of feet wide and deep. The eroded material has been spread on the valleys and plains, and has found its way to the rivers and sea. The Yellow River and the Yellow Sea are named from the color of the eroded soil which has been lost to the hinterland. So great has the erosion been that often the beds of the rivers are raised, like that of the Mississippi, until they are higher than the surrounding country. The waters tear down the hillsides in ever-increasing torrents and in China create the most disastrous floods that the world has seen. It has been estimated that the Yellow River alone transports an annual load of 2500 million tons of soil. There are other regions where rapid erosion is taking place, but the Yellow River has been described as the outstanding and eternal symbol of the mortality of civilization.

Constant farming has gradually exhausted these soils, and, in spite of a vast system of terraces which has been built up in an attempt to check erosion, the destructive forces have not been kept in control, but have devastated the loess region to the north and threatened both the soil of the plains and the lives of 100 million people who inhabit them. Untold human suffering has resulted from the periodic floods of the Yellow River. Millions have died of starvation after their crops have been washed away. The Chinese farmers have been helpless in the face of the destructive force which they and their forebears have in their ignorance let loose upon themselves. If only former generations had treated their hill forests with due respect, this great catastrophe might have been averted, but they failed to realize their dependence upon the green covering of their hills.

In the past, conservationists have pointed to China as providing the classic example of the evils of de-afforestation. It was plain that her denuded mountains were the direct cause of devastating floods and famine. But in fairness to China it should be remembered that the disintegration was slow and, bad as the position is today, China still manages to maintain a vast population, whereas other civilizations, such as those of the Babylonian Empire and Carthage, have vanished altogether. In Ceylon, Central America, and other tropical regions may be seen evidences of bygone civilizations which grew upon exploitation of the forests. But the jungle tide returned and exterminated the invaders, who had not learned the art of wooing their tricky soils.

So remote are these happenings of bygone ages that they seem unreal in these days of so-called advanced civilization. We are inclined to flatter ourselves that we can control Nature. It is thought that science and chemistry, with technical knowledge, have advanced to such a degree that they will solve all our problems. It therefore comes as rather a shock to us that the civilizations of the New World, which have developed with such rapidity, may decline with like speed. Nature is still our ruler and if we attempt to outwit or restrain her, or to transgress her laws, her answer is sterile fields and empty granaries. When we come to know this truth we shall be humbled and less inclined to point the accusing finger at China, and realize that we have all made the same mistakes. We shall have a great longing to remedy our shortcomings. It may occur to us that the present agricultural systems and methods of land exploitation, which have brought such disaster, are a modern symptom of maladjustment between man and his environment. In all humbleness and in the spirit of earnest research, we may approach the problems of China and learn from her mistakes how best to tackle the colossal tasks that today lie before the whole world.

Among the thoughtful people in China today there is a growing desire to make use of the up-to-date knowledge relating to soil conservation. China is a nation of small farmers, their average holding being no more than 4 acres. In the valleys and on the alluvial plains intensive agriculture produces rice, sugar cane, bananas, citrus fruits, and many vegetables. Hillside terracing is the common practice in many parts. This entails great labor, with meager returns. The subtropical climate of the south produces luxuriant growth both on the coast and in the interior, although in the populated areas most of the hills have long been bared of their tree covering. Here and there, however, may still be seen little ragged specimens of pines and other trees, with clumps of bamboo, poor remains of once luxuriant forests. For the greater part, rank grasses grow and provide rough grazing for the water buffalo. From time to time this grass is fired and burns any tree or shrub that may be struggling to regenerate its species. If a peasant farmer is asked why he burns the hillside, he may say that it is to scare away snakes and tigers, or to provide ash to fertilize the rice fields below. But the fires burn away the topsoil and what little humus there may be and lay bare the mineral soil, which is unproductive and easily eroded.

It must not be imagined that China is without forests. On the average every Chinese, whether he knows it or not, has nearly ½ acre of forest. In many of the densely populated agricultural sections there is actually no timber for the average Chinese. His house may be built of native clay, and often his fuel is the dung of native cattle. Even so, when he dies he must have a coffin made of wood. Ordinary coffins are made of thick planks, but the wealthy have them hewn from a single log and lacquered in black. Wood for coffins has, in fact, been one of the heaviest drains on the Chinese forests.

The camphor wood is one of the most prized trees, and fine specimens may still be found growing in association with Oriental gum and many species of leguminous trees, and with the laurel and fir families. These frequently grow on the higher slopes in mixture with native pine and Chinese fir. Bamboo is of great economic importance, because the Chinese are most clever in putting this to a variety of uses, from food to baskets or carrying poles. Freshly germinated seeds of the bamboo form an important part of Chinese meals, and often in time of famine, as in India, the bamboos seed themselves gregariously over considerable areas, and in this way, when other food is scarce, Nature comes to the rescue and provides the delicious bamboo shoots to stave off hunger.

There are more hardwoods than softwoods, and that may

help to account for the fact that China has managed to survive. It has been estimated that there are 170,000 square miles of hardwoods in the country, whereas 140,000 square miles have been classed as coniferous forest, though this by no means consists of pure coniferous stands. The total forest area of the country is 310,000 square miles, or about seven per cent of the total land area. Of this, half is classed as marketable and the other half inaccessible.

Many are the varieties of trees grown in the forests. One of the most common and most valuable is the Chinese fir, *Abies fargesii*. It is a tall tree, from 80 to 120 feet high, and at one time these trees were found up to 4 feet in diameter. The more tropical broad-leaved evergreens give place in part to deciduous northern types where altitude affects the climate. For instance, on the upper slopes of the Mei Ling are found many trees and plants typical of temperate regions—such as oak, hornbeam, birch, and maple. Broad-leaved evergreen trees grow in the more sheltered ravines, together with bamboo and many varieties of shrubs and woody lianas. Few large trees remain, but there is plenty of evidence that the forests of the hills have been exploited and burned over in the past and the dense vegetation indicates how forest cover would quickly rehabilitate the hills. In many parts the annual precipitation is as high as 70 inches a year, and, if the hills were protected from human interference, the forest cover would return.

It is essential to define land use clearly, and to keep the hills, which are the natural domain of trees, under forest types. That alone will prevent the kind of erosion which is particularly noticeable where crop cultivation has been pushed up steep hillsides. Forests will, moreover, reduce flood areas in times of heavy rains and hold back the rushing waters which carry such great quantities of good earth into the rivers, filling up the channels and blocking navigation, as well as ruining the farms and threatening human life.

Progressive fire protection, and policing to prevent fires, would in time result in the return of the forests, at least in the warm subtropical regions; but the work of restoration would be speeded up by wholesale planting and the inauguration of large-scale reafforestation. Often the will to plant is there, as is evidenced by many little groves of pine trees planted by native farmers, but so great is the need for fuel that they are often sacrificed before they are many years old. Ordinary fuel wood is desperately needed in China. Charcoal burners have made inroads into the rapidly diminishing supplies of wood, and denudation proceeds apace, with disastrous effects upon agriculture. The tide of destruction must be turned; seedlings must be planted by the millions on all denuded sites. The broad-leaved species must be encouraged as soil improvers, and an evergreen covering be maintained by the planting of such trees as China pine, which later on can be underplanted with Chinese fir as a half-shade-bearer. Any leguminous trees that will thrive should be introduced to impregnate the ground with nitrogen. Ipil-ipil, *Leucaena glauca,* a fast-growing leguminous tree successfully established in the Philippines, might well be tried in the tropical and subtropical regions of Southern China, as also acacia, *Albanesia stipulata,* which has been grown with such good results in some of the tea plantations of Nyasaland. The root system of this acacia brings up valuable fertilizing material from the subsoil, to be incorporated in the leaves which fall to the ground, thus preserving moisture and enriching the surface soil. Tree crops such as persimmon and tung oil may be planted where climate and soil permit. Nut and fruit production might well be used as a catch crop when growing forests for timber and they would reimburse the native cultivator during the years of waiting for the timber crop. It is my belief that, as a first step, an intensive educational campaign must be launched, with experimental and demonstration plantations throughout the country. The farmer must be shown that it is not profitable to attempt to grow food crops, such as rice, on steep hillsides, which are the natural domain of forests.

The Chinese farmer is a great individualist, and often he does little more than supply his own needs from his small holding. This is often scattered in small parcels, so that he spends much of his time in walking from plot to plot. His intense love of the land and individual pride in landownership rule out the feasibility of collective farming as it is practiced in Russia. Moreover, the Chinese will not sell his land on any scale large enough to allow individual owners to control and operate large tracts on rational lines. In practice it is found that ownership tends towards smaller areas, as the farms are passed on to the sons of present owners. It has been suggested that much might be done by exchange of land, but this process is slow and, even when the total land area is gathered into one parcel, it may be too small to be an effective economic unit. Part of the solution may be to encourage cooperative farming side by side with community owned forests.

The mountainous country of Korea, which was annexed by Japan early in this century, provided one of the outstanding examples of forest denudation. Originally much of this country was doubtless well wooded, as is evidenced by the remaining woodlands, which contain a great variety of species, including pines, fir, oak, maple, limes, and birch. Juniper, mountain ash, and walnut are also found, together with Spanish chestnut, hazel, hornbeam, wild plum, pear, and willow.

As were other parts of the then Chinese Empire, through centuries of bad government and misrule, together with the constant pressure of increasing population, the country was stripped of practically all its forests. When the Japanese took it over and renamed it "Chosen," after an ancient name meaning "morning calm," much of the soil subject to heavy erosion had been washed into the adjacent valleys. Many of the streams had dried up, often making the cultivation of rice impossible. Today a veritable transformation may be seen, for new forests are coming on and many of the hillsides, unsuited to farming, are clothed with a new green mantle. Already there has been real improvement in the supply of water for rice paddies, and much of the erosion on the little farms has been checked. As early as 1907 the Japanese Residency General had induced the Korean Government to undertake afforestation work, and in 1911 new forestry regulations were issued. In the same year the Governor General established an Arbor Day, and soon thousands of millions of seedlings were being planted for the purpose of re-establishing the Korean forests. The Government further encouraged the formation of forestry associations and within twenty years there were as many as 350, with a total membership of nearly one million.

Very soon there was a special government office controlling the state forests—covering between 5 and 6 million acres in the basins of the Yalu and the Tumen—and engaging in various kinds of work tending not only to improve the forests themselves, but to improve their indirect utilization. The principal trees in the forests are similar to those found in the frigid zone, such as larch, fir, birch, and aspen. Seedlings of the most suitable varieties for this region were raised in special nurseries.

The total area of forest lands in Chosen amounts to about 39 million acres, or seventy-one per cent of the total area of the peninsula; but, as it has long been neglected, the area of standing forests is estimated at about 13 million acres only, and these are mostly found in the remote north and in the eastern highlands. Of the remaining area, about 18 million acres are covered with young trees, and about 7 million acres are entirely bare.

The real problem in such regions of abandoned land is not always immediate reafforestation, but soil building, for that must precede the productive forest. The rebuilding of a forest soil involves soil surface phenomena. When there is insufficient litter cover, it is not porous enough to be capable of absorbing rain. As the north and south of the peninsula differ widely in climate, there is scope for the use of many varieties of trees. In the basins of the Oryoku and the Tumen in the north and on the higher mountains, the fir, larch, and Korean pine flourish with birch, and in the central and upper southern part the Japanese red and black pine, deciduous and evergreen oak, together with alder, are the main constituents. In the lower southern part oak and bamboo are in great evidence. The fact that there are as many as 700 varieties of useful trees in Chosen shows how well it is suited for afforestation on the widest possible scale. In recent years afforestation of hillsides and wastelands has been taken up to prevent sand drifts and to afford a future supply of timber. This work has for the most part fallen to the Lumber Undertaking Station and the branch offices of the Forestry Section, and the area so covered totals over 15,000 acres. Plantations maintained by public bodies have made great progress, and reafforestation has been undertaken by individual enterprise and development companies, many of which have started their own nurseries on a large scale.

There are many local industries which have arisen out of the forests. These are often on quite a small scale, but none the less valuable for that. Sometimes Chinese girls may be seen standing barefooted in the water of a small, swiftly flowing stream—their voluminous white muslin dresses gathered up around their waists—washing a yellowish-white batch of raw paper pulp swung backwards and forwards in a cotton sheet in the stream. The paper-pulp mill may be nothing more than a broken-down shanty with wooden tanks and vats, without any power machinery. Nevertheless, from such enterprise are produced valuable handmade papers which would favorably compete in quality with anything made in the great paper mills of Europe and the West.

Even though Western civilizations may regard such methods as out-of-date, the fact remains that China still produces quality and her slower methods have eked out her resources. But for these so-called backward methods of industry, China, the oldest civilization in the world of today, could not have survived; so let us not regard her tragedy as one that cannot be redeemed, for is not modern greed and speed hastening a far greater tragedy in a much shorter time?

15.

THE TREES OF JAPAN

T HE JAPANESE are a people who have an inherent love
for trees and it has helped them in their struggle to save the
land surface of their islands, which, but for the well-tended
forests, might have eroded away. The fact that Nature endowed the islands with so varied a covering assisted the inhabitants to preserve them. It is a miracle, indeed, that these
islands have survived so many volcanic upheavals and that
their forests have contrived to prevent catastrophic erosion,
which would have inevitably doomed them to destruction.

It is well known that the difference in the geological strata
causes variations in the soil both in kind and in nature, and
considerably affects the growth of forest trees and the formation of forests. For instance, the more primitive coniferous
forests cover an extensive area, where they retain their virgin
appearance, grown by natural regeneration on the strata of
igneous rocks, while the greater part of the forests which have
been planted are on the aqueous rocks and sandstone. The
basic stratum of Japan consists of rocks of archaean formation,
upon which the other strata have been deposited. The volcanic eruptions in each geologic period have extended over
the surface. There are large varieties of rocks belonging to the

Tertiary and Quarternary, but the largest area is occupied by andesite and basalt.

Japan's topography and climate not only affect the species of forest trees, but the condition of their growth and the composition of the forests. Extending as the country does through nearly 30° of latitude, it is natural that it should provide climatic conditions for a wide range of species. Five thousand have been named and of these nearly 300 are similar to those grown in the British Isles. There are as many as 600 species of forest trees, of which scores occupy an important position in forest economy. As much as sixty-three per cent of the total land area is classified as forest and comprises about 59 million acres. Not all of this is productive, for in the course of Japan's industrial revolution nearly 7 million acres of her forests suffered devastation through improper use and by fire. The march of Western civilization introduced new desires and industries. Japanese foresters all seem to be agreed that the political revolution in the beginning of the Meiji Era (1868) produced a disastrous effect upon the preservation of the forests. It appears that throughout the country they were mercilessly cut down, so that in all quarters of Japan hills and mountains were deprived of trees. The consequence was that not only was the economy of the forests jeopardized, but the economy of the people at large deranged, for heavy blows were dealt to productive industry in all spheres on account of the annual inundations which devastated many parts of the country. This state of affairs was particularly noticeable in the forest districts with granite strata, such as in the provinces Omi, Mino, and those portions of the Chu-gok facing the Inland Sea. The adjustment and improvement of these denuded lands called for immediate attention, and it is to the credit of the Government that *Regulations for the Provisionary Investigation of State Forests* were published in 1875. The extent of the denuded land was thus made known, and in 1877 at Nishiga-hava, Tokyo, a forest experimental station was established for the purpose of carrying out experiments regarding the cultivation of trees.

There followed a series of progressive forestry measures

which became more and more effective and have resulted in firmly establishing a system whereby the forests have increasingly benefited and the tide of destruction has been turned. Timber was soon in demand for railway sleepers, telegraph poles, and mine props, while ever-increasing quantities had to be supplied for paper pulp and a hundred and one other purposes. Nevertheless, the present total volume of standing timber has been estimated by Japanese foresters to be about 67 billion cubic feet, of which 32 billion feet are softwoods and 35 billion feet hardwoods. The estimated annual timber and pulp-wood increment is in the neighborhood of 685 million cubic feet. Systematic forest conservation has been followed with good results for many centuries and the Japanese were among the first to plant trees on a large scale. The land lends itself to extensive afforestation, and only one fifth of the whole land area is suited for farm crops. But during World War II many of the hillsides were cleared to grow food, and extensive mulberry groves, the source of the great silk industry, were sacrificed to meet the demand for more food to feed the 72 million people. The average size of a farm is a little more than one acre, and nearly half the population is engaged in farming. Land which will grow crops is so valuable that many of the farms are cropped three times a year. Fertility is maintained by the thrifty use of "night soil." This precious human excretion is collected each evening, in low wooden buckets on wagons drawn by horses or oxen, from the cities where people are fed with the produce grown for them by the hard-working farmers. The new farms made where the trees had been freshly cleared had an accumulation of humus, and this helped to solve the food problems. Moreover, food supplies came from the standing forests in the shape of wild game, acorns, nuts and other fruits, mushrooms of many kinds, and bamboo shoots. For instance, in 1945 over a million tons of acorns were collected by children, to be used in the manufacture of flour. The indirect benefit of the forests cannot be calculated in a country where the very existence of farmland is dependent on the forest for protection. So rugged is the topog-

raphy and so steep are the mountainsides that but for the
forest cover erosion would be rapid, for in regions of excessive
rainfall and winds of high velocity soil washes away and is lost,
while farmlands are destroyed by floods and inundated by
debris. But thanks to the long-term forestry practiced by the
Japanese people, vast stretches of unbroken forest mantle the
upper slopes of the mountain ranges. When areas have been
clear cut, as a rule they have at once been reafforested, over
10 million acres having been planted in the last fifty years. The
forests are classed as "utilization forests" and "protective
forests." The object of the latter is to preserve the safety of the
land and further the welfare of the people by licensing the
felling of trees. In the "utilization forests," systematic felling
and replanting take place to provide the necessary timber for
houses and the needs of industry. Felling methods might be
regarded as primitive by Western landowners, but nothing is
wasted; trees are felled close to the ground and converted in
little sawmills, of which there are between 7000 and 8000.
Both circular saws and band saws are employed in these and it
is quite common to find logs with a diameter of only a few
inches and a length of six feet being converted into planks.

The forests of Japan cover the whole range of climates, from
the torrid forest zone to the frigid. The torrid forests are
those of the whole of Formosa, or Taiwan, the southern half of
the Luchu Islands, Yaeyama, and the Bohnine Islands. Here
may be found the Ako or wild fig, *Ficus Wightiana,* variety
japonica; Tako-no-ki, *Pandanus odratissimus*; ryugan, *Nephe-
lium longana*; binroji, *Areca catechu*; tsugu, *Arenga saccharif-
era*; basho, *Musa basjoo,* and bamboos which grow vigorously
everywhere to a great size. Their strength and quality make
them much sought after for use in furniture making and buildings.

The tropical forest zone comprises Shikoku and Kyushu, as
well as the northern part of the Luchu Islands, covering the
southern part of Honshu south of 36° north latitude. Great
are the number of varieties of trees in this zone, and they
possess considerable value in the economy of the forest. As a

result of the reckless felling of trees in the past there are very few forests which retain their primitive features. In Honshu, virgin forests are found only in the neighborhood of shrines and temples.

The most important among the broad-leaved trees is the Kusu-no-ki, *Cinnamomum camphora,* which forms extensive natural forests. It is not particular as to soils, and thrives almost anywhere, with protection from cold winds. This valuable camphor tree grows in Formosa up to 3000 feet above sea level, forming pure or mixed forest with other species. The wood is hard and lustrous, retaining a peculiar fragrance, and is prized in the making of costly furniture. It is most durable and is valued for shipbuilding. The great demand for camphor has encouraged the people to make plantations of it and millions of seedlings have been distributed to encourage this enterprise.

It is not always the large trees that are the most valuable. Tsuge, the box tree, *Buxus sempervirens,* variety japonica, hardly ever attains more than about 18 inches in diameter or 50 feet in height, but the hard, uniform nature of the wood, with annual rings hardly distinguishable, is prized most of all as the material for fine carving and sculpture. This tree thrives in a limestone soil and may be generated from seed or cuttings. There are several oaks in this zone, including ichii-gashi, *Quercus gilva,* shira-gashi, *Quercus vibrayeana,* and aka-gashi, *Quercus acuta.* Of all the broad-leaved trees these three varieties are most extensively utilized, for they provide the handles of agricultural implements, and are used for building railway trucks and coaches, as well as farm carts and wagons and rudders of boats. The wood from ichii-gashi was valued from ancient times for supplying the best material for spear handles, and felling was strictly controlled by the Government. The principal deciduous oaks are kunugi, *Quercus serrate,* and konara, *Quercus glandulifera.* Both these are used for fuel and charcoal, and they are grown extensively for this purpose.

The most important coniferous forests consist of *Pinus densiflora* and *Pinus thunbergii.* The former grows thickly everywhere, from the southern extremity of Kyushu to the southern part of Hokkaido, with the exception of marshy places. It will thrive in clay or clayish soil or on dry land at high altitudes up to 6000 feet above sea level. It is one of the light demanders, is easy to plant, and is therefore extensively used in reafforestation, where it is often grown in mixture with bamboo and konara, *Quercus glandulifera*. Because of its hardy nature and rapid growth, it is often chosen by public bodies, temples, and shrines, as well as by private individuals. The wood is light reddish in color, hard and elastic. It is rich in resin, and is durable in moisture and sought after for engineering and mine props. It is second only to sugi, *Gryptomeria japonica*, as a building material, and is indispensable as a fuel and particularly popular with night fishermen, who use it for torches to decoy the fish. Moreover, one of the most popular mushrooms thrives among forests of this pine, which can be grown on poor sand almost down to the seashore, where it will stand up to the full blast of sea breezes and tolerate salt spray. In a similar way *Pinus thunbergii* has many popular uses and its rich resin content enables it to withstand exposure for many years. It is well suited to bridge building and various engineering works. As a fuel it is very combustible.

Besides these trees, there are bamboos, among the most useful of all the forest growths of Japan. They are cultivated in the private forests everywhere in that country, but chiefly in the southern part of Honshu, Shikoku, and Kyushu. These bamboos grow to enormous height at great speed; they will often attain 60 or 70 feet in a few months. Of all the bamboos, *Phyllostachys mitis* makes the most rapid growth, for it sometimes reaches one foot in diameter and 85 feet in height.

The Temperate Forest Zone ranges from the northern half of Honshu to the southern half of Hokkaido, or from 36° to 43° north latitude, and the average temperature is about 50° F. This is not only the most valuable but the most beautiful forest region of Japan. There are over sixty varieties of forest trees in this zone, among them the famous Japanese cedars, five of which are the most outstanding—namely, hinoki,

sawara, kayamaki, hiba, and nezuki. *Chamaecyparis obtusa* is
the most highly prized, and it enters more into temple construction than any of the others. The great forests of hinoki
are in the mountains of Kiso, near the center of Honda, the
largest island. The natural growth of this tree of the Imperial
Forests of Kiso is famous, and the forest is one of the three
most beautiful in the whole of Japan. Hinoki thrives best at
a height of from 1600 to 4500 feet above sea level, but it will
grow above or below these ranges so long as there is sufficient
atmospheric moisture. It will grow either alone or mixed with
other species, where it always retains its most attractive silvicultural characteristics. This beautiful cedar grows to a height
of 130 feet with a diameter of four feet. It has horizontal
branches which form a pyramidal crown, rather like its cousin,
Lawson's cypress, of the other coast of the Pacific. Its trunk
is picturesque with its deep-furrowed, or scaly, bark. The
branches are closely set with scalelike leaves. Altogether it is
a remarkably graceful tree and is particularly beautiful in its
own forest setting. The wood is dense and compact, white or
slightly yellowish in color, without prominent grain. It has
a peculiar flavor, which probably protects it against attack
from insects. It has good working qualities and, when worked
by Japanese craftsmen, takes on a satin finish, which makes
it the most popular timber amongst wood-workers. It is used
also for bridges and shipbuilding, and, above all, it is noted
for its great durability. It is stated that there are some Japanese
temples where hinoki is found in good condition after twelve
or thirteen centuries. Hinoki was used at Ise for the building
of the sacred Shinto shrines, which are a classic example of
pure Japanese achitecture, uninfluenced by Buddhism and the
Chinese School.

So many are the beautiful conifers of the temperate forest
zone, all with some peculiar or especially excellent quality,
that space will not permit their classification. Their musical
names are as beautiful as their forms and remind one of the
Maori names of the New Zealand trees. There is the hiba,
Thujopsis dolabrata, which grows at high altitudes very slowly,

the wood being white and rather like hinoki, while yet another arboristane, nezuki, is dark-reddish. Koyamaki, *Sciadotytis verticillata,* sometimes known to Westerners as umbrella pine because of its umbrella-shaped crown, intrigues botanists because it is an outstanding example of a conifer with two forms of leaves. There are the scalelike leaves, which are scattered thickly along the shoots and at the ends of the branches, and in the axils of these are clusters of from eight to twenty-five flat leaves from 3 to 6 inches in length. At first acquaintance, it is a puzzle to say whether it is a pine, cedar, or cypress.

Sawara, a cousin of hinoki, which among botanists is known as *Chamaecyparis pisifera,* and koyamaki grow together or mixed with other species at from 2700 to 5400 feet above sea level in such provinces as Yanato, Bungo, Sabsuua, Omi, Shimotsaki, and Uzen. Sawara is a light-reddish wood which is much used for carved panels in house partitions. Moni is a true fir, *Abies firma;* it loves shady places and has the peculiarity of growing much more rapidly during the latter portion of its life. The wood is light and soft, easily warping and pliable, but it finds its use for pulping.

There are many other strange and beautiful-sounding names, such as himeko-matsu, goyo-matsu, bara-momi, and kara-matsu. The last is none other than the well-known Japanese larch, *Larix leptolepsis.* Natural forests of this species are found on the slopes of the mountains of Euji and Asama and in the Azumi county of Shinano Province. This valuable tree grows on dry soil of volcanic strata, making healthy growth in the strongest sunlight, and is intolerant of shade. It will grow rapidly on the poorest of soils and it is now being widely planted to provide timber for houses, ships, telegraph poles, and engineering works. In this zone there are many varieties of deciduous broad-leaved trees, which occupy the greater part of the forest area, though they are seldom found in pure stands. The name "konara" sounds almost Irish. It is the Japanese for the beautiful oak *Quercus glandulifera.* Kashiwa is another valuable oak; so is onara. Kaba is a birch and doro-no-ki is the well-known balsam poplar. All these grow in mixture in many parts, whereas han-no-ki is the Japanese alder, which chooses swampy places. Buna, the beech, forms pure, single-aged forests which extend over Honshu and the southern half of Hokkaido. It is interesting that other varieties of broad-leaved trees grow irregularly, mixed with numerous kinds of broad-leaved trees and conifers, whereas buna will grow in pure stands, the reason being that beech is a shade bearer and will thrive under other trees, eventually taking possession of the soil, because the seedlings of the other broad-leaved trees do not have a chance to survive under the dense canopy of the beech. And yet, in spite of this, beech is recommended as a soil improver to foster the growth of other species, such as oak. At first thought it sounds paradoxical, but in practice the trees of the other species, if liable to be outgrown by the beech, are planted as many as twenty years in advance. At the end of this time lines are cut at right angles to the original rows and it is along these cleared lines that the beech are planted. The side shade provided will stimulate their growth, and up to the hundredth year there should be little risk of the beech suppressing the other species. At that stage, however, many of the beech may be tending to annihilate their neighbors, and they should be removed. The spaces thus opened out will give an opportunity for young beech to germinate and fill the gaps that have been made by the removal of their parent trees. The second generation of beech will continue the work of providing ground cover and soil improvement and in another hundred years may themselves be removed to give place to yet another generation of their kind.

Yachidamo, reminiscent of the Scandinavian tree Yggdrasil, which symbolized the universe, also an ash, *Fraxinus mandshurica,* is a tree which is grown extensively and, with katsura, may be seen all over Hokkaido. The wood of this tree has the valuable quality of durability as well as elasticity. Inuenju is another broad-leaved tree which grows in the northern part of Honshu and in south Hokkaido. This wood possesses a peculiar and beautiful luster, and is greatly valued for buildings and decorative purposes. Kurumi, one of the walnuts, likes the fertile soil of the lower land among the mountains in the central as well as the northern part of Honshu. In the plains of Ishikari, Tokachi, and Hokkaido there are beautiful forests of this walnut tree, where it grows with yachidamo, katsura, and nire, the elm. In Japan, as in the United States and Europe, the first use of the walnut is for rifle stocks, but it would be valuable for decorative paneling anywhere, and it will make excellent veneers or plywood. The wood of hari-giri, on the other hand, is white in color, and yet it is also in demand for decoration as well as for implements. In deep forests of fertile land it grows to a huge size. Kashiwa and onara are two oaks, which like the wet mountain places in the northeastern districts of Honshu, but they will also thrive in the plains of Hokkaido, where they form pure forests of oak. Kuri is the common Spanish chestnut, which is also a native of Kyushu, Shikoku, and the western part of Honshu, and it is beloved by the people of Japan for the beauty of its forests on the slopes of high mountains, where it grows in association with buna, the beech, hiba, that lovely thuya, kiwada, katsura, and also sawa-gurumi. Such deciduous, broad-leaved trees as tochi-no-ki, a kind of horse chestnut; nire, the elm; and han-no-ki, the alder; toneriko, the ash; saikachi, enoki, and yanagi, the weeping willow, are not used in the formation of forests but are valued for the purpose of creating beautiful protective belts.

Hako-yanagi, *Populus tremula,* and doro-no-ki, the balsam poplar, love moist, light soils and sunny positions and thrive wherever they find these conditions. In Monbetsu and Shari Counties of Kitami Province, in Kamikawa County of Ishikari Province, and Tokachi County of Tokachi Province in Hokkaido, they form well-developed pure forests by themselves. They grow rapidly and attain 60 feet in twenty-five years and are found most profitable, and the best wood for making safety matches.

The visitor to Japan is at once impressed with the green,

tree-covered hills and mountain slopes that are clothed almost to the sea. Those forests are of untold value, for not only are they important in the basic economy of the country, but they prevent erosion and landslides, which, but for the trees, would ruin many fruitful valleys. They hold back the heavy rainfall and release it gradually, as needed for flooding the paddy fields in the lower valleys. World War II greatly depleted these forests, and the fertility of much of the agricultural land was threatened, as the protective forest covering was removed to manufacture charcoal for war industries and rayon for clothing the people. The forests will be still further taxed for the re-building of two million homes destroyed by fire or bombs during the war, for most Japanese houses are made of wood and paper and other forest products. With meager supplies of coal, the forests provide fuel both for heating and cooking and for industrial use, and rayon made from spruce and other trees is increasingly used in clothing the people—for Japan must provide her requirements with little or no help from the outside world. Japan is fortunate in having forest resources adequate to meet her urgent needs.

The economic aspect of her forests is, however, not the most important to the people of Japan, for they look to the trees for their inspiration in daily life. They are real tree lovers and from time immemorial have shown a sympathetic understanding of the forests that protect the mountainsides and make it possible for the dense population to survive in the crowded islands. It would be interesting to discover the origin of this deep regard, which exists, not only for individual trees, but for the whole green mantle upon which very existence depends.

Of all the Japanese trees, sugi, *Cryptomeria japonica,* is the most greatly revered. This beautiful conifer, which looks so much like the big tree of the High Sierras of California, has been planted in extensive forests for hundreds of years. The world's grandest tree memorial is the forty-mile long avenue of sugi at Nikko. It was planted about 300 years ago by a Dalmyo who was too poor to offer a more costly tribute to

the shrines at Nikko. Many of the individual trees are over
five feet in diameter and in places their trunks are so close
together that they look like a wall of columns. This remarkable avenue constantly curves and bends, for, according to
ancient beliefs, any evil spirits intent on pursuing the people
would be thus thwarted and hindered.

Among the Japanese, trees are regarded as living entities
which possess spirits, and before felling is begun the spirit of
the tree has to be placated by a simple ceremony, in which the
tree's permission is asked before felling. It is significant that
the Maoris use a similar ceremony before they fell a forest tree.
They, too, are wood craftsmen of a high order. In Nippon, as
in no other country in the world, may be found the combination of that reverent love for tree and forest with a deep
artistic appreciation and craftsmanship which uses the wood of
the trees to its greatest advantage. The Japanese look to their
forests, not in vain, for shelter and fuel, as well as for almost
every kind of domestic requirement, and they depend upon
what the forest yields, harvesting it as a precious crop to meet
their needs; but never do they abuse their woodlands by reckless felling, and they always have regard to their regeneration.
They plant and tend their trees for the future, just as they
harvest and sow other crops. Before the Japanese people were
prostituted by industrialism, no people used wood so thought-
fully, or for so many domestic purposes. Their lacquered wood
bowls are beautifully turned and withstand long use, even for
hot food and drinks. No people employ the use of wood more
effectively or treasure it more highly than Japanese craftsmen,
who value the natural grain with which they ornament their
houses and temples. This reverence and sympathy, not only
for the living trees, but for the wood of the forest, springs
from their religious belief in the oneness of all living things.
The Grand Temples at Ise, simple in design and form, built
from flawless hinoki, have come down through the centuries
as evidence of a profound religious belief. No craftsman may
fell or prepare the temple trees unless he is "pure in heart."

Western civilization, with its rush for gain and craze for mass production, may well take a lesson from the Orient, where man can still live close to Nature and where reverence is paid to the natural resources of the earth.

16.

THE MAGIC ISLANDS

To THE traveler the islands of the Pacific are steeped in romance and they never fail to cast a mysterious spell over his mind, whether he or she visits them by air or sea or is introduced to their charms by a travelogue film, or the pages of a treasured book. The very mention of their names is as music: Hawaii, Tahiti, Rarotonga, Bali, Java—these are as notes in an entrancing symphony. Many travel stories have been written about them, and many are the romantic pages which have depicted the life idyllic among the aborigines who bask on sandy beaches under the shade of palms, laze in their canoes, or dive in clear waters filled with bright-hued coral and little fish of many colors. Many are the coral reefs, decked with a patchwork of angelic green, bordered by waterways of deepest blue. Here are entrancing lagoons studded with little islands, where coconut palms wave their fronds and bananas and pineapples grow with superb luxuriance unequaled elsewhere.

At one time, maybe, these magic islands were part of a mighty continent which may have been the motherland of the world. Recent research has brought to light a growing volume of evidence to show that this continent did exist. Its tragic disappearance has not yet been fully explained, but it either subsided or was eroded away, leaving but mountain peaks visible above the water. Coral reefs have formed around many of these fascinating islands which we would visit.

If one were to set out from the East Coast of Africa, the spice island of Zanzibar would be the first port of call. This is the home of nutmeg and cashew—tiny by comparison with Madagascar, the fifth largest island in the world, which is about four times as large as England and Wales, for it is close on 1000 miles long and over 350 miles in its greatest breadth. In days gone by, when man was yet young, the forests of Madagascar were religiously guarded. It was the sacred duty of the king, who was also high priest, to protect the trees and forests, particularly where they formed catchment areas at the sources of springs and rivers. Primitive man soon came to recognize the close association between trees and water and his dependence upon both for his existence. That might well account for the protection of the forests from earliest times in Madagascar.

It is interesting to note that there are no family names in this island and that almost every personal name is drawn from the language of everyday life and signifies some common action or object, such as a tree, a plant, or a bird. This is evidence that the people, or the ancient rulers, were aware of the kinship of man with every living thing. This custom had its drawbacks, for, such was the reverence paid by the island dwellers to their kingly priests that, whenever one of these words was taken as the name of their chief it became sacred and could no longer be used for the object it denoted: hence a new name had to be invented. It is little wonder that the visitor meets with language difficulties!

The dried-up beds of ancient lakes would indicate that in times gone by the hills were better clothed with forests than they are today. Even now the lake regions are fertile and well wooded, especially on the eastern side of the island, though a large district in the southwest is barren. Erosion and soil deterioration might have been worse but for the fact that all round this mountainous island is an almost unbroken belt of forest, from ten to forty miles across, containing many trees treasured for their timber and forest interest. Here we find the traveler's tree, *Ravenala madagascariensis,* the raffia palm, the lace leaf, the beef-wood tree, *Casuarina equisetifolia,* several species of small pandana, and bamboo. Three fourths of the species and one sixth of the genera of the plants are endemic, or native only to Madagascar, showing that the island is of great antiquity. About 4100 indigenous species are now known, and there is a single family with twenty-four species confined to the island. There is scope for large-scale afforestation, particularly on the east and northeast, and the Malagasy are likely to follow any lead given, for they have an inherent regard for their trees and forests, around which many a folk tale has been woven.

There is magic in the very remoteness of the 100 tiny islands of the Seychelles, where grows the largest fruit in the world. It is one of the palm coconut trees, *Lodoicea seychellarum.* Its gigantic fruits take six years to develop. Inside the shell are found two or three nuts and it is popularly known as the sea coconut, or coco-de-mer.

Ceylon has a land area of 25,500 square miles, and a total forest area of over 16,000 square miles, three quarters of this being unprofitable or inaccessible. Tea plantations cover much of the land, which was at one time primeval forest. Coffee, which itself is a forest tree, was the first popular plantation crop in the early days of British colonization. Sir Samuel Baker's farm in Nuwara Eliya was among the best known, but disease resulting from the wholesale clearing of the forests and the introduction of monoculture cost Ceylon £15,000,000 and destroyed the popularity of coffee as a crop, and tea took its place. Forest growth is strong, and many ancient buildings and temples have been swallowed by the jungle, which has reclaimed land where people once lived in crowded cities.

To a visitor it would seem that this enchanting island was "draped with forests of perennial green," for the hills tower magnificently until they are lost in clouds and mists. Undulating plains cover four fifths of the island, while one fifth is occupied by the mountain of the Central South, which rises to 8000 feet above sea level. Most of the trees of Ceylon are found nowhere else in the world, though some of them, and many of the plants, are closely allied to those of the Malay islands and peninsula. The trees are evergreen and form thick jungles with gregarious plants known as nilu, a species of *Strobilanthlae,* which flower at regular intervals of five, six, or seven years. In the mountain forests, tree ferns luxuriate to a height of 25 feet. Scarlet-flowering rhododendrons add to the beauty of the natural bush.

In the low-lying country coconut palms are much in evidence, and a beautiful areca palm, the feathery jaggery, or kitual, and the lordly talipat are among the species which enhance the glories of the vegetation. Calamander, satinwood, and ebony are among the timber trees of special value. In the dry forest region in the north of Ceylon may be found the palmita, or Trincomali wood, and ebony. The characteristic palm of these regions and the Peninsula of Jaffna is the palmyra, *Borassus flabelliformis.* The coconut, cinnamon, and several species of pepper are native to the island.

It is to be regretted that extensive cutting of the forests has denuded the mountainsides, the trees having been felled for the purpose of making plantations. The improvident practice of native shifting cultivation known as *chena* has also been responsible for denuding much of the island. When I visited Ceylon, I had the privilege of broadcasting in three languages and urged the hill cultivators to plant trees on their old farms before forsaking them to make fresh ones, and of recent years the Forestry Department has met with some success in persuading the people to establish in this way potential forests for the future.

Before leaving this enchanting island, I must mention that high among the mountains near the ancient capital, Kandy, are the famous Peredinia Gardens. These gardens, which are the Kew Gardens of the East, contain one of the finest collections of tropical trees in the world. For many years the curator has published a book describing the plants and trees of his arboretum with concise notes for their cultivation. As a forest officer in Equatorial Africa, I found this book invaluable whenever laying out a new station. Years afterwards I had the pleasure of spending some days in the gardens near Kandy, and was able to see the numerous species of trees growing side by side, and to study their various characteristics at close range. I am so indebted to the curators of this beautiful arboretum that I feel bound to pay this tribute for the great contribution they have made to planting, not only in Ceylon, but throughout the tropical and subtropical regions of the earth. There is great scope in Ceylon for an active branch of the Men of the Trees to carry on an educational campaign, among both planters and indigenous peoples.

There are two groups of islands in the Bay of Bengal, the Andamans and the Nicobars, which together formed a province of British India. They contain dense tropical forests, and the climate is warm and moist with heavy rainfall. There are many islands off the Malay Peninsula, which itself contains 41,390 square miles of forest, or 78.8 per cent of the total land area. About 40,770 square miles of this consists of hardwood trees and only 620 square miles of conifers. Before World War II Malay produced half the world's supply of rubber.

Sumatra is the largest of the great Cunda Islands and is nearly as large as Spain, for, with the many islands along its coasts, it is probably 180,000 square miles in extent. The Equator runs through the middle of it and the greatest length is 1115 miles. This great island has its own mountain system, with several ranges towering to 1200 feet above sea level with intervening plateaus and valleys. Geologically speaking the kernel of Sumatra consists of slates and clay schists of high antiquity, with granite sometimes visible; but the whole has been modified by strata of the carboniferous formations, and in later periods by Tertiary breccias, sandstones, marls, and coral beds. Volcanoes have played an important part in embossing the surface and, only sixty-four years ago, the southern end of Sumatra was involved in the great Krakatao eruption. The lovely mountain lakes are largely volcanic. Many of these have been formed by the craters falling in on themselves in the manner of Crater Lake on the northwest Pacific Coast of America. The rivers are fed by an abundant rainfall, which may be over 80 inches a year, and the humid climate and volcanic soil produce ideal conditions for tree growth.

There are at least 400 varieties of timber trees native to the island, and vast areas of the mountain regions are covered by virgin forests as yet not fully explored by botanists and foresters. The total forest area has been estimated at 113,000 square miles, or about six times that of the forest area of Spain, for nearly sixty-three per cent of the total land area is forest. The climate and soil make Sumatra particularly suitable for agriculture and plantations. Rice is a staple crop, and sugar is grown from canes and arage palm, while coffee and coconuts, as well as pepper, sago, maize, sweet potatoes, and yams, have long been cultivated. As recently as the beginning of the twentieth century, extensive rubber plantations have been made and nearly half a million acres planted.

The forests of Java and Madura are 10,000 square miles in extent and comprise nearly twenty per cent of the land area, which is 51,000 square miles. These mountainous islands have forty-three volcanoes, several of which are still active. There are four distinct botanical zones, the lowest of them being characterized by tropical forests, with palms and mangroves which flourish between high and low tides and in tidal creeks. The second region is that of the plantations, where tea, coffee, cinchona, sugar, and maize are grown. Grasses, herbs, and shrubs are characteristic of the third zone and the fourth is alpine. Many are the varieties of trees to be found, as might well be expected in a country with such a great variety of climate and aspect. Oaks have been known to thrive above an altitude of 4500 feet, while in Sumatra they come down to 500 or even 100 feet above sea level.

In the short space of a century the population of Java has sprung from about 9 to 50 millions. An ever-increasing demand will inevitably be made upon the forests, and permanent protection forests will be needed to regulate water flow.

There is a strange custom sometimes practised when rain is wanted. Two men will select supple rods and flog each other until the blood flows down their backs in imitation of rain. Fraser suggests that the prophets of Baal, who sought to procure rain by cutting themselves with knives till the blood gushed out, may have acted on the same principle. A simpler and more humane way of assuring precipitation is to plant trees.

Next to Greenland and New Guinea, Borneo is the largest island in the world. To reach it from the south, the Java Sea is crossed. The length of the island is about 800 miles and its breadth 700; it contains a total area of 284,000 square miles. The northeastern part is occupied by the states of Sarawak, Brunei, and North Borneo; its total land area is 84,000 square miles with a total forest area of 73.7 per cent. The country is mountainous; the highest points range from 4000 feet to 8000 feet; broadly speaking, the whole country is corrugated and gnarled in a most irregular manner. This is the result of the process of denudation carried on by the tropical rains, which, through the ages, have scooped out interior valleys and plains and laid down vast level tracks that extend eastwards into the morasslike delves.

Major Patrick M. Synge, who was a member of the Oxford Expedition to Sarawak, in his book, *Borneo Jungle,* describes the forests as "so luxuriant that they seemed a frenzy of greens, a solid wall, a never-ending skyscraper of leaves overhanging the water's edge, behind darkness and mystery." Borneo is indeed a superb forest country. The giants of the tropical forest are often festooned with woody lianas and many choice orchids or pitcher plants may be found by the explorer. The people follow the practice of shifting cultivation. They hack their way into the jungle, and clear areas in which they grow their food crops. After they have reaped them, they move on to repeat the same destructive process. When the paddy field is left deserted, the ground soon becomes reclothed with tropic vegetation. Whereas it is possible to walk through the virgin forest, it is necessary to hack a way through the dense jungle that takes possession of such clearings.

The forests produce many and valuable trees, including iron wood, bilian, teak, ebony, sandalwood, dye woods, and the camphor of Brunei, which is the best in Asia. The mohur tree, which is a popular timber, reaches a height of 80 feet, and the kaladang, which is much sought after for shipmasts, reaches a height of 200 feet. Nutmegs, cloves, cinnamon, pepper, ginger, and sugar cane are among the many crops that are cultivated. When we think of those deep tropical forests, we are apt to conjure up a mental picture of a paradise of many blossoms which vie with each other in the brightness of their coloring, whereas, in fact, one has to hunt for the flowers of the trees. Even if one is fortunate enough to find a fallen blossom on a forest trail, the canopy of the forest denizens is so closely inter-woven that it is quite a feat to determine the tree from which it came. Many tree flowers are ridiculously small in comparison with the flowers of other plants, and some are quite incon-spicuous.

The glory of the tropical forest is the shimmery green of lux-uriant foliage, contrasting with greens of more somber hue. But there are times when the explorer becomes satiated with beauty. There is monotony in the evergreen rain forest, for there is none of the freshness of foliage that springs to clothe naked branches in colder climes, nor is there any temperate autumn to transform the leaves into bright colorings. Through-out the year there is little variety, for there is no pause in the growing period, the high temperature and high humidity encouraging unceasing growth; it is perpetual summer. The rings by which a tree records its age in temperate countries are unknown. The work of colonization goes on in the treetops, and here, unobserved by man, seed production is carried on by brightly colored butterflies and many tiny insects, which assist the trees to perpetuate their species. Life in the treetops is dazzlingly beautiful; the dance of life goes on in timeless space. There is a ruthless rhythm in the intensity of growth, where

everything germinates and begins to thrust its way upwards in
bloodless conflict for a place in the sun. The earth itself is a
child of the sun, and its tree children are ever striving to get
nearer their distant father. In Borneo and other volcanic
islands of the Pacific we are reminded of this, for the thermal
energy is nearer the surface. This generates electro-magnetic
currents which stimulate growth.

Borneo is a plant collector's paradise and provides a largely
unexplored field for botanists. There is a lure in the green
glory of its forest fastness which will call the traveler back to
further exploration.

The Philippine Islands, named after Philip II of Spain, form
a northern section of the Malay Archipelago, separated from
the rest by the Sulu and Celebes Seas. Of the total land area of
115,000 square miles, the forest area is 40,000 square miles;
38,000 square miles are hardwoods and 2000 square miles
conifers. The islands were discovered in 1521 by Magellan,
during his great voyage round the globe. Legaspi, who came
from Mexico in 1565, established a Spanish colony in the
islands. In the succeeding centuries, the colonists had to defend
themselves against the Portuguese, Chinese, Dutch, English,
and Moors. After the destruction of the Spanish Fleet by
Admiral Dewey at the time of the Spanish-American War in
1898, the Philippines were ceded to the United States. Under
American rule the islands experienced administrative and
economic advancement, and the achievement of American
foresters does credit to the American Forestry Service. The
names of Aheren, Pinchot, Bryant, and others are well known.
During visits to America I had the privilege of meeting both
Major Aheren and Gifford Pinchot. The latter was the first
forester of the United States to be appointed by Theodore
Roosevelt at the time of the inauguration of the forestry service. He is better known today as the former Governor of
Pennsylvania, but his early contribution to the science of
forestry will always be remembered. These men were great
pioneers in the field of forestry, both in the Philippines and
in their native land. It was their vision and courage, backed

by scientific knowledge, that provided for the mapping out of the forest areas of the Philippines, island by island, when the lands were classified and working plans drawn up between 1905 and 1913. Among other pioneer foresters were Merril, Whitford, Foxworthy, Matthews, Merrit, Cuzan, Shfersesne, Nash, and, last but not least, Corran, to whom I am indebted for bringing these names to my mind. Those young men came fresh to their new colony from the remnants of American timber lands. They had seen the spoliation by lumbermen in their own country and were determined that the forests of their new possession should be put on a sound footing and be saved for all time for the people of the Philippines. Under the wise administration of Arthur Fischer, now Colonel Fischer, the last American chief of the Philippine Forest Service, these forests, which are among the finest in the world, were placed on a sustained-yield basis under scientific management. Before the fateful incident of Pearl Harbor, the Philippines possessed an efficient staff of Filipino foresters, who were trained for the most part at the School of Forestry at Los Banos. It is earnestly hoped that many of these young men have survived the war, for in their hands will rest the future of the forests in the Philippines. The war made great demands upon those forests for all kinds of construction materials and fuel wood for sugar mills, as well as alcohol for the Japanese transports. Many of the young trees planted by the students of the forestry school were cut by the Japanese for bridge building and for wooden ships. The school plantation included teak and Honduras mahogany over 100 feet high. Many of these trees were sacrificed during hostilities, but, fortunately, the bulk of the forest wealth of the Philippines remains and is now helping to heal the scars of war. It is to be hoped that the future of one of the most wonderful hardwood forests of the world will be safe in the hands of hundreds of trained Filipino forest officers, who will see to it that the wealth of their woods is economically harvested and regenerated for perpetual use.

The same warm currents that touch the eastern coasts of

the Philippines sweep northwards to the shores of Formosa, where there are splendid primeval forests covering the greater part of the island. Of the 13,900 square miles of land area, 11,000 square miles is forest.

Far out in the Pacific are the Ladrones or Mariana Islands, a group of fifteen discovered by Magellan. The five which are to the south are low and flat; those to the north mountainous. Most are thickly wooded and all are well watered and fruitful. Timber is exported from Guam.

The Caroline Islands, another group in the western Pacific, are all fertile and well watered, and many of the low-lying lagoons are well wooded.

A contrast to these tiny islands is Celebes, the third largest and the central island of the Malay Archipelago. With its adjoining islands it is variously estimated to contain an area of from 72,000 to 78,000 square miles and has about 19,000 square miles of forest, which approximates to twenty-six per cent of the total land area. To the north the Sea of Celebes separates this great island from Borneo. It is a Dutch possession with numerous small native states. The east end of the eastern peninsula is subject to earthquakes and contains eleven volcanoes, some of which are active; for instance, Mount Sapoetan, 5938 feet, and Mount Klabat, which reaches a height of 6559 feet. There are numerous hot springs and sulphur lakes in this mountainous volcanic area. The highest mountains are Latimojong, which is 11,470 feet, and Lombo Batang, 10,000 feet. The uplands of the southern peninsula have the best forests. The crops include rice, maize, coffee, sugar, tobacco, indigo, areca, betel, pepper, clove, and nutmeg, which last grows wild. The Macassar oil tree, ebony and sandalwood, oak, teak, and cedar are among the better-known trees. The Minahassa district is famous for producing coffee of a remarkably fine flavor.

The Bugis and Mangkassars of the South Peninsula, tall, with fine figures and comparatively fair in complexion, are the dominant native race and are good sailors.

Away to the south is Timor, with a range of wood-clad

mountains that runs throughout the island chain, stretching eastwards from Java, with a total area of about 12,000 square miles; but its comparatively dry climate produces less luxuriant vegetation than that of Java.

The greatest island of Australasia is New Guinea, formerly known as Papua. This great tropical forest land is separated from the Continent of Australia by the shallow, island-studded Torres Strait, only eighty or ninety miles wide at the narrowest part. There is no doubt that the two regions at one time formed continuous land and it has been suggested that an upheaval of less than 60 fathoms would again unite them.

New Guinea appears to have been first sighted by D'Abreu in 1511, and first visited by De Meneses about 1526, and again by Alvaro de Saavedra in 1528. It was named from the resemblance of its inhabitants to those of the Guinea Coast of West Africa. In 1914 it was occupied by an Australian force, and the Commonwealth of Australia holds it by mandate. It is essentially a mountainous country with lofty ranges, its highest mountain being 13,000 feet. There are elevated plateaus, which are used as health resorts by the officials and traders from the coast. The whole of New Guinea lies in the track of the southeast trade winds, prevailing from March to October and charged with much moisture from the Pacific. These are followed for the rest of the year by the northwest monsoons, whose rain-bearing clouds are condensed on the cooler alpine slopes of the islands, so that the rain- or snowfall is considerable in every part of the country. This, combined with an average high temperature of from 80° to 90°, results in a hot, moist climate on all the low-lying coastlands and river valleys, making them suitable for large-scale afforestation.

Great is the variety of trees found after passing through the domains of tropical plants. Such temperate or subtropical growths as the cedar, oak, fig, acacia, pine, and tree fern are found on the higher slopes, and with them may be seen wild strawberries, forget-me-nots, daisies, buttercups, and other familiar plants. Toward the summits, these are succeeded by true alpine flora, in which Himalayan, Bornean, New Zealand, and sub-Antarctic forms are numerously represented. In general, tree vegetation ceases at about 11,000 feet and shrub at 12,000, the latter being overlapped by the alpine zone. In New Guinea it is found that the Asiatic Malayan floras are far more richly represented than the Australian, as is demonstrated by the rare occurrence of the eucalyptus. Indigenous forms are numerous and include many species of palm. Of the total land area of British New Guinea, which is 170,000 square miles, as much as 136,000 square miles is forest, or over eighty per cent. It is sparsely populated, for there are 97 acres per head of population, whereas, for instance, in Japan, there is considerably less than one acre per man.

East of New Guinea are the Solomon Islands, which stretch southeast in two parallel chains for 600 miles towards the Santa Cruz group. They have a total estimated area of 17,000 square miles, 10,000 square miles of which is forest. There is an extraordinarily heavy annual rainfall, estimated at 400 or even 500 inches on the mountains and 150 on the coasts.

New Britain, an island of the Bismarck Archipelago, separated from the northeastern coast of New Guinea by the Dampier Strait, is well wooded in the interior. With the other islands of this Archipelago, the total land area is 20,000 square miles, half of it forest. The native folk are famous for their handsome canoes, with sails and outriggers. The interior is little known to botanists, and there is great scope for the plant hunter.

New Caledonia, belonging to France, lies midway between the Fiji Islands and the East Coast of Queensland. The Loyalty Islands, Isle of Pines, and some others, with a total area of 1250 square miles, are politically dependent upon New Caledonia, which is 6450 square miles. Below its mountain summits the forest covering is generally unbroken and contains many useful timber trees.

The New Hebrides group consists of thirty islands, most of which have the appearance of being well wooded, but, with a total area of 5700 square miles, 700 only are classed as forest.

The Fiji Islands were sighted in 1643 by Tasman, the great Dutch sailor after whom Tasmania has been named. But, like many of the South Sea islands, the Fiji Archipelago was little known before the nineteenth century. The islands are from 200 to 250 in number and lie in a ring open on the southern side in a manner resembling the West Indies. The total area of the colony is given as 7083 square miles—or about the same size as Wales.

The Fiji Islands are of volcanic formation, surrounded by coral reefs which form natural breakwaters and good harbors. The rainfall is abundant in the warm season, and the land is most heavily timbered on the southeastern, the windward side of the islands. On the leeward side the country is largely open grassland. The islands have considerable agricultural resources. All these islands and many hundreds of others, some of which are entirely of coral formation, such as the Marshall Islands, east of the Carolines, and the Gilbert Islands, are to be found in this largest of oceans, which occupies one half of the water surface of the globe and more than one third of the whole area of the world.

17.

KAURIS AND MAORIS

WITH THEIR primitive grandeur, the kauri trees of New Zealand form a living link with past ages and in their delectable home, cut off from the rest of the world, their forests have not been invaded by mammals or other forms of aggressive life until recent times.

For millenniums, surrounded by his lesser tree brethren, the giant kauri has reigned in the green glory of his forest domain. He and his sires of bygone ages experienced land upheavals and submersions and yet remained to re-establish their evergreen kingdom on the new land as it rose out of the sea. From his forest sanctuary he looked on snow-clad mountain peaks while he felt the warmth of subterranean springs and his growth was nourished by volcanic ash from the underworld. This king of forest trees has survived all cosmic changes, and today, in his arboreal majesty, shares honors with the Californian sequoia, a veritable patriarch among trees.

The kauri pine, *Agathis australis,* not only is the most outstanding tree of New Zealand but in the quality of its economic products and scientific interest rivals all other living trees. The realm of the kauri pine is between latitudes 35° and 37° south, which corresponds to Melbourne and Valparaiso. It is farther south than the Cape of Good Hope, though I believe it would thrive in Cape Colony. In the Northern Hemisphere, it would be on the same latitude as Tokyo, Wei-hai-wei, Chitral, Teheran, Gibraltar, the Grand Canyon, and Monterey. With the co-operation of the countries in their zones it would be interesting to plant groups or belts of kauris, with their natural nurse trees, around the world. Its seed is contained in a cone, 1½ to 2 inches in diameter, made up of a number of flat brown scales, each covering a single scalelike seed. It grows naturally in mixed forests of shade-bearing species where there is a luxuriant growth of other lesser plants; these it overtops when it reaches its full height.

The largest kauri is reputed to have been 93 feet in girth, but the greatest tree reported with certainty was 66 feet in circumference and 100 feet to the first branch. This massive tree contained 30,000 cubic feet of wood. The timber of such a tree would weigh about 500 tons and would contain enough planks one inch thick to cover an area of nearly 5 acres. The largest kauri now standing is approximately 51 feet in girth, with an estimated volume of about 17,000 cubic feet.

Besides timber, they yield a valuable gum. I once saw a Maori climbing one of the bigger trees to collect gum from the forked branches and he seemed to be walking up it with as much ease as a fly walking up the wall of a room. He had iron points in the toes of his boots and was armed with two hammer-shaped axes—rather like a mountaineer's ice pick—one of which he carried in each hand. These he drove alternately into the trunk of the tree to help himself up, using the sharp points in the toes of his boots as climbing irons. He carried a rope with which he let himself down as soon as he had collected the gum. This precious gum, much sought after for varnishes, is sometimes found beside the root of these trees, where it has been buried under the surface for many years. It is also dug up from the ground or dredged from swamps, where forests of these trees have formerly grown, and even lies mingled in the cold stratum of the Tertiary deposit. The new gum is whitish in color, but in time it turns a dull amber. Often tiny flies and insects are seen embalmed in the middle of a lump. The finest quality is used for amber beads. During the past century, over twenty-two million pounds' worth of this so-called minor forest product has been exported from the kauri forest region.

A remarkable feature of the kauri is its trunk, which has hardly any taper, but grows a cylindrical bole over 100 feet high, surmounted by an umbrella-shaped crown of olive-green foliage. Unlike the redwoods and many conifers of the Northern Hemisphere, which have conical forms and drooping branches to provide protection against snow break, this tree does not need much protection, for the aspect of its forests is tropical.

I shall never forget my first sight of these lordly trees in the Waipoua Forest. They stood in the virgin bush, which had been opened up by a clearing, so that their mighty buttresses appeared to form a colonnade. Overawed by their kingly dignity, I felt that I might have been standing in an ancient Greek temple, for their huge trunks stood out in clear-cut relief backed by the somber green of lesser forest growth.

Although the lower parts of the trunks were usually branchless, they did not give the appearance of being bare, for these patriarch trees acted as hosts to a number of climbing ferns, lichens, and hanging grasses, while air plants and orchids draped their massive columns. Tough, woody lianas hung suspended in the air and bushes, trees, and shrubs of every kind formed a tangled mass to cover the ground around their buttresses.

There was an incessant struggle for life, silent and serene. As I entered the forest parthenon, rays of light shot through the foliage and sunbeams danced on the fronds of climbing ferns and pendant grasses, and dappled the gray-brown trunks of those ancient friendly trees. They seemed to be beckoning me on into the inner recesses of a quiet world where time is not. I found myself standing close to the oldest tree of all. As I touched the gnarled old bark, I tried to visualize the happenings of the past. He had looked out on the glorious sunset of a former day. His forebears may have been planted by the giants of a past age. Eleven generations of his family had germinated, grown, and fought their way up through the tangled growth, looked out over the treetops where they reigned for 1000 years, and then returned to earth to complete the cycle before being reincarnated in their grandsons. For 110 centuries the silence of the forest was unbroken but for the note of the bellbird and his many feathered friends. Flightless birds there were in plenty, including the giant moa, which stood over 12 feet high, with legs the strength and size of those of a horse. He could not fly, but he had no enemies from whom he needed to escape; until one day, about 600 years ago, canoes were sighted and men who hunted the moa arrived on the scene. The silence of 100 centuries was broken and for the first time the sound of the ax was heard. Kikaumako trees were being cut to make wood for men's fire-sticks. Other men were collecting dead sticks to cook their food. These men were the Maoris, who had come in their double canoes, sailing the ocean for 1600 miles until they looked out on what they called "The Land of Ao-Tea Roa," or the Land of the Shining Coast. They brought with them their wives and children and dogs, as well as rats, which they had used for food on their long voyage. They found a flax plant, *Phormium tenax,* growing on the fringe of the forest, which they cut and from which they prepared fibers for making their garments. At first they obtained all their food from the sea and the forest, and made no farms, so the balance of Nature was not upset. The only clearings they made were for their *pas* or fortified villages. These they made with birches and tawa, and their canoes from the rimu, or red pine. They looked on the trees as their brothers, and would not unnecessarily harm them. Was not Tane, the Lord of Light, father both of the trees and of man? Their priests had taught them the ancient lore that trees were the first living things; they felt their kinship with the trees through their common father. When a Maori went to the forest to seek a tree for a new canoe, he would first ask its permission before felling it and then cover up the stump with foliage so as to protect the inlying spirit.

Life in the forest went on much the same as of yore, and the giant kauri looked out on the doings of these men with unconcern for another 300 years. The coming of Tasman, the Dutch sailor, in 1642 was a mere incident. As he looked upon the Shining Coast, it seemed to him that it had recently risen out of the sea, and he called it "New Sea Land." He came, but he did not stay, and so the forest once more became tranquil. Nearly 150 years later the English arrived, and for the first time the sound of steel axes was heard. Their brand of civilization made heavy demands on the forest, for they needed farms in which to grow their food and pastures for their flocks and herds. Soon the conservative methods of the Maoris were discredited and their simple ways of conservation were upset by the newcomers. Maoriland seemed ripe for exploitation. Its climate reminded these colonists of England, and its forests provided a challenge to their way of life. At the beginning of their settlement the kauri forest was growing over a large part of the North Island from Tauranga nearly to North Cape. It was felled without any regard for its future, and, as in all pioneer stages of European settlement, far more forest was destroyed to clear lands for farming and grazing than was ever cut into timber. But they used it for every domestic purpose, and exported it to the Australian colonies.

New Zealand proper has an area of 103,656 square miles; though smaller in size, in configuration it is not unlike Japan. It consists of two large islands called simply North and South, and a number of small islands and islets, some of the latter lying in tropical Polynesia, where the Cook group and Niue, Penrhyn, and Suwarrow Islands have been annexed to the Dominion. New Zealand also governs most of the Samoan Archipelago and, with Great Britain and Australia, shares the administration of the phosphate-bearing island of Nauru. Her Governor-General's sphere of influence extends to the Antarctic territory of Rossland.

Of the great forest area that once clothed the hills and valleys, only 20,700 square miles remain today, 10,600 square miles of which consist of conifers and 10,100 square miles of hard woods. Fortunately, more than half of the remaining total forest area is classed by timber men as unprofitable or inaccessible. Nevertheless, those great areas serve their invaluable function of moderating the climate and helping to distribute and conserve the rain and melting snows. Twenty per cent of the total land area is still forest, and there are over 8 acres per head of population. The natural features of the land are full of variety and interest; it is healthy and fertile and its scenery is magnificent. There are long and lofty mountain ranges with more than 150 peaks or cones exceeding 7000 feet and in South Island sixteen rise to more than 10,000 feet. In the southwest of that island much of the Southern Alps are in the eternal snows, and their highest peak, 12,349 feet, is Ao-rangi, the Mountain of the Sky, as the Maoris call it. Settlers called this peak Mount Cook, after Captain Cook, who, in 1769, landed at Waykanae Beach close to the present site of Gisborne. Mountains cover the greater part of South Island, running in close parallel chains from southwest to northeast. As in England, there is more rain on the west coast than on the east; the rain-bringing winds from the southwest and northwest are caught by the spinal ranges, so the country eastwards is comparatively dry. For instance, the rainfall at Christchurch is about the same as Norwich in East Anglia, 26 inches, while that of Holitika is about 116 inches. In North Island the mountain chains, though lower, show similar features.

All the forests of New Zealand come into the category of *rain forest*, which may be divided into two distinct classes, subtropical, or rain forest proper, and sub-Antarctic, the former allied ecologically to tropical rain forest, and the latter dominated by species of *Nothofagus* as the only tall trees. Their habitat extends through nine degrees of latitude, and they occupy a vast area which is situated chiefly in the mountains and hilly parts of both islands and on soil usually unsuited for agriculture. With the exception of Totara the wood has not been greatly used, though it is one of the most important of all the indigenous trees. On the other hand, the subtropical rain forest has been greatly reduced in area, because it is considered that the land on which this forest grows becomes at once greatly enhanced in value when the tree covering is replaced by meadow. The wood of these species has been much in demand to make packing cases for the famous New Zealand butter. The transformation from rain forest to sheep pasture and dairy land requires but one year for its accomplishment. Through this remarkable fact the wealth of the Dominion in large measure has been won—but at what a cost! Approximately 14 million acres of forest have been felled and sown to grass in New Zealand. Not all of this has been successfully converted grassland, for at least 2 million acres have reverted to secondary growth and scrub forest. It has been calculated that 4 million acres of standing forest awaits "development."

When it is considered that so large an area has already been deprived of its forest cover, it is remarkable that the country has so far been spared from serious erosion. It is true that a great deal of soil wash was prevented by sowing grass seeds on the "burn" and the climatic conditions were favorable to rapid germination, so that the grass was able to establish itself before there was any serious damage done by rain or wind. At any rate, the destruction of the virgin forests, from whatever cause, has been carried to a dangerous length. Many of the hills are now growing an inferior type of grass which does not provide adequate covering, and after a heavy downpour the murky streams are a danger signal which should be heeded.

It is the very isolation of New Zealand that makes it of interest to the student of forest ecology. In that country may be seen every transition from virgin-tree communities to completely artificial ones. The land is rich in ecological experiments of various kinds, such as the burning of vegetation, different methods of agriculture, the presence or absence of certain exotic mammals, the fencing of a piece of ground, or the incoming of a new weed. Northern weeds are a serious pest. Gorse and broom introduced by the colonists are rampaging over millions of acres, weeping willows have choked many streams, and weeds, like other things, seem to grow more vigorously than in their native land.

The student has an opportunity of studying the various stages of draining swamps, or witnessing a virgin forest turned into a sheep run. Even a neglected farm will provide valuable data and furnish splendid material for studies of great importance and intense scientific interest. It is possible in a day's ride to study the deterioration of land from virgin forest through successive years of farming or grazing to examples of erosion and landslides.

Perhaps nothing is of greater interest in New Zealand's plant ecology than the effect of the multitudes of grazing and browsing mammals of many kinds upon a vegetation which had come into being unprepared for such an invasion. For some time many of the forests were immune from their attacks, but now there is one great herd of deer from some distance north of south latitude 30° to south latitude 47.20°.

It is to be regretted that once the original forest cover has been removed it will not return naturally and often less valuable species take its place.

Rimu, or the red pine, *Dacrydium cupressinum*, is one of the most outstanding timber trees in New Zealand and covers about forty-five per cent of the forests. The three Podocarps, miro, *Podocarpus ferrugineus*; matai, *Podocarpus spicatus*, and totara, *Podocarpus totara*, contribute five per cent each. Two hardwood birches, tawa, *Beilschmiedia tawa*, and tawhai, or red beech, *Nothofagus fusca*; Southland or silver beech, *Nothofagus menziesii*, and clinker beech, *Nothofagus truncata*, form some thirty-seven per cent of the remaining economic forest. All the evergreens are valuable timber trees. The total cut in 1935 was 244 million cubic feet, of which rimu contributed over half. It is a strong building timber and a beautiful cabinet wood; its color is reddish or yellow, it takes a high polish, and it is very ornamental. Matai is very fine-grained, reddish in color, and when exposed after cutting becomes so hard that it is difficult to drive nails into it. Totara and kahikatea are softer; the heart wood of totara is very durable in the ground. Kahikatea, New Zealand white pine, *Podocarpus dacrydioides,* is much used for backing veneers and plywood, and it is rather like our northern pines. Other timber trees are kawaka, *Libocedrus bidwillii,* and Westland or silver pine, *Dacrydium colensoi.* The existing forests might well be extended, for they create their own microclimate and, if they are to be preserved for all time, the natural conditions which favor their growth must be given due consideration.

One of the most popular exotic species of tree now being planted is the well-known Monterey pine, *Pinus radiata,* which flourishes on the pumice lands near Rotorua. Its growth is astonishing, being five times as fast as on its native peninsula in California. A forty-six-year-old plantation will yield as much as 207,000 board feet per acre. Douglas fir, *Pseudotsuga douglasii,* from the northwest Pacific, is somewhat slower in growth, although much more rapid than in Washington or British Columbia. Ponderosa pines are now being planted in increasing numbers and so are redwoods, which may in time exceed in growth that of their parent trees in the High Sierras.

It remains to be seen whether in the long run it is a good policy to sacrifice the native trees for fast-growing exotics. In monoculture there is always a grave risk of attack by parasites or pests, which may sweep the whole area. Besides, these pure stands alter the character of the country, so that it no longer enjoys the serenity or dignity of the mighty forests which once cast their magic spell over the land.

18.

AUSTRALIA

WHEN I WAS a boy, Australia always held a strange fascination for me: I come of pioneering stock and my forebears had gone to the Dominions and Colonies and had even placed whole countries on the map. Major Baker, who was a soldier by profession and a sailor by inclination, had thrice sailed round the world in his own yacht on voyages of discovery, but none of my family had ever settled in Australia. And so in my childish fancy I wondered whether it would be my good fortune to go to that great continent where men could still be pioneers. "Woodcraft" and "bushcraft" were words which meant a whole lot to me, although in those days the only chance I had of playing at bushman was in the pine and beech woods which were around my home in Hampshire. My father, who had never had the opportunity of traveling farther than the South of France, had a sincere regard for what he called "Colonials"—men of our stock who had blazed the trail of overseas settlement in the great Dominions. The very fact that Australia seemed so far away held out a challenge to me, and for that reason I took an inordinate delight in any story about that remote country. I was twelve years old when the Commonwealth of Australia came into being and the six colonies became known as states. But Canada was the first country to claim me, and it was not until fifteen years ago that I visited that land "way down under." It was then I realized that Australia, with its 2,974,600 square miles, was 800 square miles greater in extent than the whole of the U.S. From the geologists I learned that Australia was physically the oldest of the continents. It is a great plateau on which there are few elevations rising more than 2000 feet above the sea. They told me that Mount Kosciusko, whose present height is just over 7000 feet, was once higher than Everest, 29,000 feet, but it has eroded away. The antiquity of this country is confirmed by its trees and other vegetation, for most of the trees are of primitive type existing elsewhere only as fossils, or in coal measures. Among the most primitive found are the *araucarias*, monkey-puzzle trees. Eucalyptus has by far the largest number of timber trees, for there are about 235 species, which range in height from dwarf trees of 2 feet to giants of 326 feet. One of the tallest is the *Eucalyptus regnans* from Gippsland. They are known as gum trees and their timber varies in color from almost white or pale cream to pink, red, or brown. Many of their barks are quite smooth and almost white and others gray or green, while some, such as the "ribbony" gums, *Eucalyptus viminalis*, have fibrous and stringy bark. Eucalyptus is in fact a most important and widespread genus. English names are applied loosely to different species in different districts; for instance, one of the largest eucalyptus trees known to me is called "giant mountain ash." The particular tree I have in mind stands about forty miles from Melbourne. I believe it may be the largest tree, not only in Australia, but possibly in the whole of the British Empire.

Wattles, or acacias, include about an equal number of species, and they are the most characteristic flowering trees and shrubs of the tableland bush, and their flowers are used as an emblem of Australia. There is a wealth of flowering trees, many of them eucalyptus, especially in Western Australia. Queensland has its tulip tree, *Stenocarpus*. Then there is the Illawarra flame tree, *Sterculia*, and the Western Australian fire tree, *Nuytsia*.

There are a large number of timbers of economic value, and the pleasing dramatic effects of many of the ornamental, fine-

Gum Trees Near Wilpina, Australia

It is Fascinatin
Watch a Big Ele
Pick up a Log—
Burmese Teak Fo

Modern Man is M
Increasing Deman
the Wealth of
Mighty Forests

Much of the Southern Alps is in the Eternal Snows—The Fern Track
to Franz Josef Glacier, South Island, New Zealand

This is the Realm of Great Conifers—Deodar, Himalayan Cedar, at Chakrata, India

ere the Glacier Meets the Timber Line

Contrasts: Log Jam on Montreal River, and

Sand Dunes in Argentina

Among the Magic Islands

The Forest is the Mother of the Rivers

The Beginning of Water Erosion in an Abandoned Field

On the next two pages:
A Close-up of Lumbering in Sweden

The Timber-line in the Rockies

Aborigine Climbing a Eucalyptus Tree, North Queensland

A Pond on a Well-wooded Estate at Dunmow, Essex, England

Water is the Source of Life—A Scene in the English Lake Distric

From a Painting by Vagaggini

grained woods have yet to be fully appreciated. Some are finding their way into modern buildings, not only in the towns of
their native land, but in other countries. Some have been used
most successfully in luxury liners and in railway carriages. The
New South Wales turpentine tree, *Syncarpia*, is used for bridge
piles and eucalyptus has been used successfully in the building
of harbors, for it offers considerable resistance to toledo borers.
Among softwoods are the Moreton Bay pine, araucaria; the cypress pine, *Callitris*; the red cedar, *Cedrela*, or cigar-box cedar,
and the red and black beans, *Dysoxylon* and *Castanospermum*.
Rosewood and silky oak are popular furniture woods in the East,
sandalwood in the West, and blackwood, *Acacia melanoxylon*,
in Victoria and Tasmania. The beauty of many of these woods
when skillfully converted has to be seen to be believed.

Unfortunately, the virgin forests from which these trees come
have been exploited with too little thought for future supplies.
The lands which contain such valuable trees should be worked
on a sustained-yield basis, so that supplies of their timbers may
be available for all time. There is a danger that, when the virgin forests are felled, inferior species may take their place, for
there has been a tendency to pick out the plums, or the trees
that are most sought after for the beauty and usefulness of their
wood, and leave the rest, with the consequence that the forest
deteriorates, never to regain the natural composition which
yielded those treasures. The major task of the forester is to provide his fellow men with raw materials that are indispensable
and bound to become more valuable in the future. Besides that,
he has the task of maintaining a tree cover on those soils which,
in consequence of their physical characteristics, can be used only
for forests. The way in which whole mountainsides have been
deprived of their tree covering is humiliating to thoughtful
people. When an earthquake razes man-made buildings to the
ground, we are quick to deplore the tragedy and hasten to repair the damage; but when man destroys the finely balanced
economy of Nature to satisfy his greed, we refer to it as "developing the country."

It was a tragic time for Australia when in 1788 the British

Government decided to transport convicts from the crowded prisons and, later, Irish rebels in shiploads to that continent. On these ships sailed colonists who had not been convicted of crimes, and they began to "open up" the interior. The more orderly convicts were allowed to serve as laborers on tickets-of-leave. The foundation of convict settlements in Australia had established the fact that Europeans could live there and colonists reached it from the British Isles in ever-increasing numbers, till the stream became a flood when gold was discovered in the middle of the nineteenth century. In accordance with the habits and tradition of their race, the settlers demanded the right to manage their own affairs, and they did, but with the disastrous results that may be witnessed in their land today. The inoffensive native inhabitants, who had been forest protectors, for their wants were few, retired in rapidly dwindling numbers into the arid and tropical regions in order to escape from the invaders. Ruthless destruction of the forest began, and in their ignorance the colonists soon upset the balance of Nature. In their blindness they did not see that the forest was their friend, and treated it as an enemy to be overcome and routed. True, the pioneer took his life in his hands when he declared war on the big trees. Felling big timber is dangerous work, especially when the tops of the mighty trees are entangled with creepers. These tough vines, with which the whole jungle is interwoven, are a menace, for a falling tree may bring with it the tops of other trees yards behind in the very direction in which the axman is jumping for cover. Again, a hollow tree is apt to upset the calculations of the most skillful axman, and may crush him as it falls to earth in a splintered mass. Great Australian eucalyptus trees sometimes take their revenge in the moment of their fall.

"Civilized" man is, however, diabolically ingenious in the way in which he brings destruction on himself and his descendants; for, not content with felling a tree here and there to meet his needs, he must devise a skillful plan by which he can destroy as much as an acre of high forest in a fraction of the time it would take him to deal with the individual trees. His devilish device saves him much chopping, especially in hilly country where trees should never be clear-felled. This fiendish practice is known as a "drive." The axman will lay into the trees in such a manner that each will fall on its neighbor, when the pressure from above is set off by a big "drive" tree on the uphill side of all the others. When the fate of the trees is sealed, they do not break off where they have been cut but are shattered in all directions. Beautiful timber which might have brought shelter and happiness to many generations of men is torn to splinters, while the forest echoes with shrieks and explosions, and mother earth, who bore the trees, trembles under the impact of their giant bodies. Tall timber may be felled over 100 acres or more at a time, and left until the end of the dry season, the ground covered to a depth of 20 or 30 feet with splintered trees and branches. The whole of this lies on a deep bed of dry leaves and rich humus, which has been gradually accumulating on the forest floor for 1000 years. When the farmer is ready to set fire to the prepared area, he makes a torch with oil-soaked hessian and applies it along the foot of the clearing. The flames rush up the slope with a deafening roar. Dense rolling clouds of black smoke rise upwards towards the heavens. Terrific heat is generated, and the oil of the trees produces a highly inflammable gas which may quickly fill a whole valley and ignite with a deafening explosion, hurling burning trees into the air like matchwood. The heat thus generated is so fierce that the earth is severely scorched, and rocks explode as though there were an artillery bombardment. The man-made fiery hurricane gathers speed, lifting burning logs and hurtling them through the air like leaves in a whirlwind, which explains why such a forest fire will cross a valley at the speed of an express train. Soon the sun is blacked out, veiling destruction as the fire rages and sweeps on. No one who has not witnessed such a fire in Australian high forest can appreciate the speed of destruction or the amount of damage involved. Just a clearing to make a farm to grow fodder to feed cattle, which are killed to feed man. Thus man destroys the sylvan temple which God did plan and build.

When the Australian farmer uses the term "planting," he usu-

ally means sowing grass seed or farm crops. This is done after
the felled forest has been burned off. Should rain happen to
fall before the "planting," the ashes form a hard surface, making
it impossible for the seed to germinate, so the sowing is generally done directly the flames have died down and while many
fallen trees and stumps are still burning. This task is not without its dangers, for many farmers have been severely burned.

Almost anything will grow without cultivation in this ash
from the trees that have protected and enriched the soil for a
thousand years, though these methods are nothing less than de-
spoiling the earth of the stored-up wealth of the ages. But the
damage will have to be made good under threat of the extinction of humanity. Scientific forestry must become the fundamental economical factor, because it is necessary in order to assure
a balance of climate and hydrography, without which a lasting
civilization is impossible.

Dr. Halliday Sutherland records that since pioneering days
"down under" the water table, as ascertained in the sinking of
wells, has continuously fallen with the destruction of trees to
make room for sheep and other farming. At one time there was
a veritable fresh-water subterranean sea under much of Australia. The trees there sent down their roots to almost incredible
depths through the subsoil to reach it and could not otherwise
have lived through long droughts. Now, even when not directly
destroyed by man, they die because the water table has sunk
farther than they can reach.

I have the greatest admiration for individual pioneers, both
men and women, who have played their part in the drama of
this old yet new continent. They have wrestled with floods,
drought, fire, and disease in flocks and herds. They have faced
loneliness in the great open spaces, and but for their courage
and resourcefulness they would not have survived. But often, in
ignorance, they have brought destruction upon themselves and
have left behind a heritage of denuded lands. A new generation
must arise who, inspired by love of the earth, will work and
replenish where their fathers worked and exploited.

Fortunately, there still remain noble forests in their primitive state. Many of the eucalyptus grow so closely together that their tops are interwoven and appear to form a continuous canopy. When one flies over such a forest, it looks as if it would be possible to travel for miles along the treetops. It is slow work walking through a eucalyptus forest, and nobody who has no experience of virgin forest can appreciate the difficulty that it offers to penetration. Any forest survey in these regions is a laborious task, and one must be prepared to forego the direct route because of the impenetrable nature of the undergrowth. The dense canopy is made all the more compact by a mass of leafy lianas which ramify among the treetops. Under such a forest roof it might be imagined that ground growth would be suppressed and that a clean forest floor would be found; but, on the contrary, this is covered with tangled growth of evergreen plants, shrubs, and woody vines, which form a dense bush and obscure the sunlight. It is heart-breaking work to walk any distance, for it is impossible to avoid entanglement by creepers and thorns, which tear the stoutest clothes and pierce the flesh. Massive trees, felled by past cyclones, further impede progress.

Once I attempted to walk along the bole of a fallen giant to escape the surrounding jungle; but just as I was beginning to feel the relief of having defeated the murderous thorns and tangled undergrowth, the bark gave way and I dropped into a pulpy mass of decayed wood and fungus. There is no such thing as keeping a straight course in a eucalyptus forest, for to make any progress at all it is necessary to be constantly looking for diversions. Only the skilled bushman can keep his bearings and hope to arrive at his destination. There are times when even the bushman is defeated by the jungle and it is no wonder that many dauntless ones have lost their lives when traveling under arduous conditions. But the forest has its language, and those who can read its signs may steer a desired course. The bushman knows how to find the points of the compass by the nature of the vegetation. He has observed that generally northern and eastern slopes are matted with the luxuriant growth of lawyer and raspberry vine, while southern slopes are covered with tree ferns and clusters of lilies. He knows, too, that the southern side

of a tree is more often covered with moss and lichen, while the
northern side shows a clean bole. He is helped by his knowledge of the trees and shrubs in any given area, and he knows
that at the foot of the mountain ranges a certain species will
bloom some weeks earlier than the same species on the higher
slopes. At 1000 feet it will be blooming, while at 2000 feet it will
still be in bud. Knowledge of the snow line may also provide
a useful clue, and by such means it is possible to estimate the
approximate altitude.

I shall always remember with a sense of deep satisfaction my
visits to Australian virgin bush, of which there is all too little
left to meet the needs of this expanding dominion. Although
I had grown many millions of eucalyptus trees for my forest
plantations in Equatorial Africa, until a few years ago I had
not the chance of studying the eucalyptus family at home in
their native bush. The thing that impressed me more than anything else was the dense evergreen ground cover which protects
the floor of the forest and prevents too much evaporation. Eucalyptus is a light-demanding tree, needing the ground protection which it enjoys in its native habitat. It is axiomatic to say
that the amount of vegetation varies with the rainfall, but the
height and quality of the timber grown may depend upon the
type and density of the ground cover. Along the eastern coast
and inland to the foothills of the main range extends a well-
timbered region; but as the rainfall lessens and the ground
cover changes, the character of the timber varies from the soft
woods of the great coastal "brushes" to the hardwoods on the
range and foothills. The coastal forests have a dense undergrowth, while on the ranges this tends to disappear, and in the
foothills there are grand expanses of rich pasture land, park-
like in appearance, with groups of fine trees.

In Western Australia, in contrast to Eastern Australia, there
is an important forest belt on the inland side of the main range.
Here may be found the popular jarrah and karri eucalyptus
trees. Where the rainfall is under 20 inches, forest growth ceases
and the scrubs of the plains take over. Many are the varieties
of shrub eucalyptus that cover dry, but otherwise fertile, land.

Next to this type come stunted and scattered trees with little herbage, while in the central area appear plant forms such as saltbush, *Atriplex* and *Rhagodia,* and spinifex and nardoo, which provide fodder in times of drought; the last, a crypto-gam, *Marsilea,* is used by the aborigines for food.

Rainfall is not the only factor controlling vegetation. Uniform climatic factors prevail over large areas and the land relief is not, in general, enough to bring about marked changes in "local climate," so that a particular plant community often stretches unchanged for a great distance. It has been noted by those who have made a study of vegetation in the semi-arid and arid regions of Australia that the changes of plant community within an area of uniform climate are mainly determined by edaphic or soil factors and have to do with the amount of soil water, or are associated with change of geological formation. The country is divided into pastoral holdings of several hundred to over 1000 square miles. It is difficult for Americans to appreciate the extent of the Australian farms or ranges: 640,000 acres is no mean holding! Such holdings are called "stations" and are divided into "paddocks," usually 12,000 or 13,000 acres in extent. In the study of the forest regions, the human factor looms large in the more settled areas. In Victoria and Tasmania, for instance, the vegetation has completely changed, owing to interference by man. In a few years the climax forests of *Eucalyptus regnans* which have covered the rolling hillsides may be entirely replaced by continuous sheets of *Pteridium,* the weed which in these parts covers worn-out potato fields.

Following the removal of the high forest with its dense ground covering, the rainfall tends to become less evenly distributed. When a storm breaks, run-off quickly brings erosion to the land. Gullies are among the more spectacular results of erosion which play havoc with hilly land, while rolling land is rapidly ruined by the more insidious and widely destructive process of sheet erosion. It has been demonstrated that when gully formation has begun, the land has already lost much of the most important element in soil fertility and stability—namely, the water-holding capacity of the soil. This is apart from the actual soil material which has been lost by wind and rain. In Australia, generally speaking, the water-holding capacity of the soil is confined mainly to a few inches on the surface, where fresh humus formed from decaying leaves and animal remains accumulate. Sheet erosion, by removing the most absorbent layers, not only speeds up the run-off water which is the chief eroding agent, but decreases the value and shortens the period of usefulness of the rainfall. In a country where every drop of rain is needed to maintain life, this factor of erosion is more serious than the actual loss of soil. Hence the clear felling of wide expanses of high forest to form sheep runs and farms has started a vicious circle. The devastating droughts of recent years would not have been so serious fifty years ago, for much of the rain would have been held by the absorbent soil and utilized in the dry season. Today, after years of forest destruction, an abnormal rainfall is necessary to produce the same results that might have been obtained from a moderate rainfall while the protective covering was still there. Now, a high rainfall tends to wash away more of the remaining soil than a low or moderate one. Where erosion is under way, heavy downpours of rain are an added danger and it seems that in many parts of Australia drought conditions are past remedying. Much has been said of the Dust Bowl of the Middle West of the United States of America, but little is known of the extent or speed of water erosion and the growing desert in Australia. The wheat lands of New South Wales are the most extensively and seriously damaged areas. This is due to the fact that wheat is mostly grown on undulating land which should never have had its forest covering so drastically removed. Again, the climate conditions are more conducive to erosion. It has been observed that in Victoria, South Australia, and Western Australia the rainfall tends to occur more in winter, and the intensity of individual falls is therefore not so great. In New South Wales, summer thunderstorms are more frequent and more intense, with greater ensuing damage. The obvious remedy is to reafforest all hilly country and make pastures of undulating land, establishing frequent shelter belts of forest trees, which would be a valuable asset to every station. The reclamation of desert and arid regions would provide work for tens of thousands of planters, who might be trained in the particular technique required for such a vast and difficult undertaking. The efforts to study the arid vegetation at Koonamore under the supervision of the University of Adelaide on a sheep station of over 1000 square miles, with an average rainfall of only 8.45 inches, will be watched with interest.

Research is needed to discover what species can best be grown in shelter belts in such arid regions. The more arid parts of the Soviet Union may contain a number of plants of various types which would be of service in the work of land reclamation in Australia. However, there is no doubt that hundreds of useful trees and shrubs for desert planting might be found among the 147 natural orders that are represented in the native flora. The forest is the most useful servant of man. Not only does it sustain and regulate the streams, moderate the winds, prevent droughts, and beautify the land, but it also supplies wood, the most widely used of all natural products. Its uses are numberless and the demands that are made upon it by mankind are numberless also. It is essential for the well-being of mankind that their demands be met, but the length of time required for the growth of a forest shows conclusively that it was never destined in the order of Nature for the exclusive use of a single generation. Even though great cities may be built from the profit resulting from the exploitation of virgin lands and forests, Nature will exact her payment. If the Dust Bowl of the Middle West was the price exacted for the skyscrapers of New York, Australians may well ask themselves what the bill will be for theirs.

19.

SOUTH AMERICAN VISTA

SOUTH AMERICA is linked with Australia through her
trees, even though the countries are divided by the greatest
expanse of ocean in the world. A tree tribe which spans the
Southern Seas is one of the most primitive gymnosperms: it is
the *Araucarineae*. These trees were flourishing at the same time
as the giant reptiles who laid their eggs on dry land and were
independent of water for breeding purposes. In a similar way,
the members of this tribe of conifers with a hard-coated seed
depended on air and wind rather than water for their reproduction, so there must have been a land bridge at one time.
There are about ten species of araucaria, inhabitants of South
America, Australia, New Guinea, New Hebrides, New Caledonia, Norfolk Island, and New Zealand. The long mountain
ranges of the Andes are covered with mixed evergreen forests,
dominated by conifers. Beginning at 36° south latitude is
Araucaria imbricata, now so well known in Great Britain and
other parts of the world. Unlike its New Zealand cousin, the
giant kauri pine, it will stand frost. Although treated as a
curiosity in European parks and gardens, in Kenya it has been
successfully planted as a forest. These tall evergreen trees are
distinguished from the other conifers by having a single ovule
on a simple scale. The araucarias are unlike any other tree in

the world. How can I describe these lordly trees, which tower to heights from 100 to 160 feet? Their straight, cylindrical stems lift their broad, umbrella-shaped crowns of very crowded branches high over the heads of lesser forest denizens. Their bark is very rough and divided into curious scales: it is a perfect child's puzzle of slabs of different sizes with five or six distinct sides to each, all fitted together as neatly as a honeycomb. The branches are at first very spreading, and in young or isolated individuals they persist for a long time. In the forests they generally fall off, leaving only their crowns, which are a striking sight.

Their leaves are all of one kind, spirally crowded on the branches, rigid, ovate-lanceolate in shape, with a sharp point at the apex. The leaf is slightly concave on the upper surface, glabrous, and shining, bright green in color. If a still closer examination is made with the help of a lens or a microscope, it will be seen that each leaf is marked with longitudinal lines and has many stomata on both surfaces. The margins of a leaf are cartilaginous. The leaves of this curious tree persist for ten to fifteen years, and only begin to wither during the latter part of their life. For a long time after a leaf has fallen, its remains may be seen on trunk and branches as narrow transverse ridges.

The male flowers are catkins, almost cylindrical in shape. They are either solitary or two to six in a cluster, and are erect, 3 to 5 inches in length, yellow in color, and composed of densely packed anther scales, the tips of which are sharply pointed and recurved; there are from six to nine pollen sacks. The extraordinary thing is that the male flowers frequently remain intact on the tree for several years, though generally in Europe they appear only in spring, the pollen escaping in June or July. The female flowers are ovoid in shape, and one only is born at terminal shoots. It, too, is erect, about 3 inches long, and is composed of numerous wedge-shaped scales which terminate in long, narrow, brittle points. After fertilization, the cone takes two years to ripen, though three months after its fertilization the seeds are fully mature; there are about 300 seeds in a cone. Nature has been very cautious with the Chilian araucarias, for she has not only protected the trees with formidable armor, but even the fertilizing apparatus and the cones themselves are covered by a thick brown coat.

It is interesting to make a close study of the seedling. The cotyledons are two in number and on germination remain below the soil enclosed in the seed. The caulicule, to which the cotyledons are attached, is thick, fleshy, and carrot-shaped, serving as a store of nutritious food for the plant after that of the cotyledons is exhausted; it is directed downward into the soil, and terminates in a long, slender, fibrous root, which gives off a few lateral rootlets. The plumule, the portion of the axis with its accompanying leaves which is formed in the embryo prior to generation, protrudes between the stalks of the cotyledons, speedily becomes erect, and develops into the young stem, which bears leaves similar in shape to those of the adult plant. Some time after the stem has grown above ground, the cotyledons wither away, the ends of their stalks being visible on the upper part of the caulicule. At the end of the first season, the stem is 4 or 5 inches long and bears alternate leaves about ¾ inch long, gradually increasing in size from below upwards, and a crowded tuft at the summit, a pattern of things to come. The lower end of the stem is reddish, with leaves small and scalelike. The fusiform caulicule, about one inch in length, is continued below into a root 8 or 9 inches long.

Now what about the sex of this remarkable tree? The araucaria is usually dioecious, the trees being either male or female. There are some who believe that there is a difference in the habit of the two sexes, but a careful study has shown that araucarias differ remarkably in habit and no inference can be drawn as to sex from the habit or character, or from the growth of an individual. Monoecious trees, as is the case in nearly every dioecious species, are of exceptional and very rare occurrence. Augustine Henry noted that these occurred at Bicton, the seat of Lord Clinton, and in the gardens of Lytchett Manor, near Poole, belonging to Sir John Lees, Bart.

This curious tree was discovered about 1780 by a Spaniard, Don Francisco Dendariarena, who was employed by the Spanish

Government to examine the trees in the country of the Arau-
canos in the south of Chile, with the object of finding out those
trees whose timber was best suited for shipbuilding. His account
of its discovery, as quoted by Lambert, is as follows:

> In September 1782 I left my companion, Don Hippolito
> Ruiz, and visited the mountains named Caramaviva and
> Nahuelbuta, belonging to the Llanistha, Peguen, and Arau-
> cano Indians. Amongst many plants, which were the result
> of my two months' excursion, I found in flower and fruit
> the tree I am about to describe.
>
> The chain or cordillera of the Andes offers to the view
> in general a rocky soil, in parts wet and boggy, on account
> of the abundance of rain and snow which falls in these re-
> gions, similar to many provinces in Spain. There are to be
> seen large forests of this tree, which rises to the amazing
> height of one hundred and fifty feet, its trunk quite straight
> and without knots, ending in a pyramid formed of hori-
> zontal branches which decrease in length gradually towards
> the top, is covered with a double bark, the inner five or six
> inches thick, fungus, tenacious, porous, and light, from
> which, as from almost all other parts, flows resin in abun-
> dance; the outer is of nearly equal thickness, resembling
> cork cleft in various directions, and equally resinous with
> the inner.

It has been suggested that the district mentioned by him is
not really part of the Andes at all, but a close range separated
from the Andes by a wide tract of low country, mostly covered
with forest. The tree was first fully described by the Abbé Mo-
lina, who called it *Pinus Araucania*. Ruiz and Pabon, who explored parts of Chile soon afterwards, sent specimens to Europe
to a Frenchman named Dombey, which were described by La-
marck under the name of *Dombeya chilensis;* but the genetic
name he gave cannot stand, because it was previously used for
a genus of *Sterculiaceae*.

In 1795 Captain Vancouver, after whom Vancouver Island

was named, visited the coast of Chile, accompanied by Archibald Menzies, who was medical doctor to the expedition and who procured some seeds which he sowed on board ship and succeeded in bringing home as living plants. These he gave to Sir Joseph Banks, who planted one of them in his own garden at Spring Grove and sent the remaining five plants to Kew. One of these, after being kept in the greenhouse till about 1806, was planted out on what is now called Lawn L and was at first protected during winter by a frame covered with mats; here it grew for many years and attained a height of 12 feet in 1836, but eventually died in the autumn of 1892 at the age of nearly 100 years.

It did not, however, become common in cultivation till the celebrated botanical traveler, William Lobb, who was sent to South America by the well-known nursery firm of Veitch, sent home in 1844 a good supply of seeds which produced most of the finest trees now in England. In their native habitat they grow in scattered groups on the cliffs at an elevation of 3000 to 4000 feet, or scattered among coigue or beech trees, *Fagus dombeyi,* and higher up in a forest among niere and another beech, *Fagus antarctica.* With them are about four podocarp pines, *Fitzroya patagonica,* and in the extreme south quite extensive forests of at least two species of incense cedar. Remnants of these forests extend northwards into Peru and across the Andes into Argentina. They are at their best in boggy valleys, where the ground underneath is enlivened with purple and pink everlasting peas, beautiful terrestrial orchids, and other plants. They do not always have such flat tops as those of Brazil, but are more domed, like those in Queensland. It is a wild and rugged country in which they thrive amid huge gray boulders covered with moss, and here and there a profusion of wild flowers. They look out over the snowy cones of the Cordillera, which pierce their way through the long line of mist and often hide the nearer mountains from sight. On the windswept ridges at 6000 feet the araucarias are more stunted, and have a different habit of growth. The geographical range of the tree is a very limited one, extending only from Antuco in about latitude 38° 40′, to latitude 40° in the Cordillera, and on the coast range from about latitude 38° 30′ to an unknown point, probably not south of about latitude 41°. The soil on which they grow is mostly of volcanic origin, sometimes covered with deep vegetable mold, but more usually dry and rocky. The climate, though warm and dry in the months of December, January, and February, is cold and wet in winter. There are two types of araucaria forests, one of which is characteristic of the rainy coast mountain range of Nahuelbuta and the west side of the Andes on the Cordillera of Pemehue; the other is peculiar to the drier plateaus of the Argentine territory on the east side of the watershed. In the museum of Santiago there are geological evidences of the existence in a former period of araucaria as far north as the Puna of Atacama.

Chile is divided by Nature into three separate zones, each with its distinctive climate and industrial interests. First the northern zone, which consists largely of sandy, arid deserts, and is also a region holding vast mineral wealth, particularly copper and nitrate of soda. Then comes the central region, comprising fertile agricultural valleys, traversed and watered by numerous rivers running from east to west. There are also active industrial districts. Last, the third of the zones, where the central valley lies and the coastal range is transformed into a vast archipelago—here sheep and cattle are raised and virgin forests abound. Comparing these three topographical features of Chile with those of other parts of the world, it may be said that the northern region is much like the desert sections of North Africa, both in coloring and configuration; the central zone like the State of California; and the southern zone similar to Norway.

General Arthur Goodall Wavell, grandfather of Field Marshal Lord Wavell, is conspicuous among those who helped the country towards independence. His vision embraced political co-operation of all nations of the hemisphere and his life was dedicated to the welfare of the peoples of Latin America. It is not surprising that his grandson wrote a glorious page in the history of the world's struggle for the principles of liberty and justice.

Speaking at the World Forestry Charter Luncheon held in London for representatives of the Diplomatic Corps at the Dorchester Hotel on April 9, 1946, the Chilean Ambassador, Señor Don Manuel Bianchi, said:

> For the second time it is my privilege to attend the gathering of the Men of the Trees, the Society founded in 1922 by Mr. Richard St. Barbe Baker.
>
> At last year's meeting a plan was submitted for a World Charter for Forestry, containing many useful suggestions for the general preservation of woods, the reafforestation of uncultivated land, the employment of large stretches of water, legislation for the prevention of forest fires, the creation of National Parks and improved education in forestry, etc.
>
> I passed on to the Chilean Government the Society's memorandum and am happy to tell you that the idea of such a World Charter for Forestry is warmly welcomed in my country. Chilean forestry legislation is in many respects identical with that suggested in the memorandum in question. Chile, especially in the southernmost part, is one of the most richly wooded countries in the world and my Government, aware of the present-day need of timber for the reconstruction of the devastated zones of Europe, does everything possible to increase and preserve this richness.
>
> I offer my congratulations to Mr. St. Barbe Baker for his initiative in putting forward the idea of a World Charter for Foresty, which I hope will be realized in the very near future.

Nominally, Chile, with its 200,000 square miles, has a total forest area of 60,000 square miles, but actually there is only about 8000 square miles of what would be termed commercial forest.

Flying over from the Argentine I was struck by the tremendous amount of forest that was being felled. Large tracts had been cleared to make farms, and I was reminded of the similar devastation I had seen in New Zealand. Little information is available about erosion in South America, for it is still in the advancing, pioneering stage. The cream of fertility is being fast extracted from the Argentine pampas, but so far only the farsighted are concerned with the trend of exploitation. For many days I traveled across the continent from Buenos Aires to the Andes, and I became alarmed at the extensive removal of forests. The soil fertility in the Argentine is known to be decreasing, on account of the continuous removal of animal products and the neglect of the use of manures and natural compost. The classical example of mountain terracing in Peru stands as a lesson to modern soil miners. The latest reports from the Argentine state that there are approximately 193,000 square miles of forest, or seventeen per cent. Felling is permitted only in the case of trees which have reached a state of maturity and since the Forestry Directorate assumed its functions one of its primary considerations has been the reafforestation of cutover Government forests by the transplanting of trees from nurseries, or by direct sowing. These operations are now being put into effect for the first time under the supervision of Demonstration Forestry Stations.

As I sailed up the Plata, our ship scraped her bottom on the silt which had come down the river and its tributaries, not only from the felled forest areas of the Argentine, but from the lands of Paraguay and Uruguay and Brazil. Paraguay, with its 162,000 square miles, is said to contain 43,500 square miles of forest, and Uruguay, which is 72,000 square miles in extent, has a total forest area of 2300 square miles, or just over three per cent of the total land area. Bolivia, with 514,000 square miles, has 197,000 square miles, or thirty-seven per cent of the total land area. But wherever I went I saw that severe inroads were being made into virgin forests, and in my opinion I nowhere saw large-scale reafforestation. The cause of the silting up of the mouth of the Plata is the denudation of the hinterland which is drained by this great river and its tributaries. The entrance to the fine harbor of Buenos Aires is kept open only at a great cost by dredging. A farsighted policy would support large-scale reafforestation of all steep land and mountainsides, and plant up the banks of all rivers with species to fix the soil and prevent water erosion. But this would call for the concerted action of all those countries I have mentioned. National feuds and rivalry would have to be sunk in this great task. The fertility of these lands and the preservation of their waterways can be maintained only with close international co-operation.

Much of the land is a natural domain of forests. At the first World Forestry Charter Luncheon held in London in 1945, over which Lord Sempill presided, the Argentine Ambassador, Dr. Don Miguel Carcano, gave a valuable lead when he stressed the vital importance of forestry in his country. He recognized the necessity of planting both to safeguard the valuable timber resources of the Argentine and to prevent soil erosion. His Excellency described many of the most interesting trees and mentioned one that is as hard as steel. He said that they knew how to cut it, but so far they had not discovered the silvicultural treatment required for regenerating it. He suggested that it presented a problem to the World Forestry Committee.

The largest and most valuable evergreen forest in the whole of the Southern Hemisphere is that of the Paraná pine, *Araucaria angustifolia,* which is situated on the east watershed of the Paraná River in Brazil and extends into Paraguay and Argentina. Paraná pine is the Brazilian araucaria. It grows in mixed tropic and semitropic forests on the cooler elevated highlands forming the upper story of the forest and shading a great variety of lower-growing hardwood trees. The total area of Paraná pine has been estimated at 300,000 square miles, with commercial stands covering 100 million acres, meaning perhaps a total stand of 40 billion cubic feet. It is an excellent softwood timber, taking the place of northern deals, and it is reported to be good for pulp making. With this pine are two podocarps, these three species being the only conifers so far found in Brazil. Growing in their native habitat, these trees form a really beautiful type of forest. They are like great umbrellas opened out to shade the lesser forest denizens. Their trunks are straight, and the older trees are free of branches below their widespreading crowns. Trees have been found up to 8 feet in diameter.

but 3 feet is more usual, and logs 60 to 80 feet in length may be considered average. The proximity of the Paraná pine forests to the great rivers Paraná and Uruguay and their tributaries makes logging easy, and at the rate of exploitation it will not be so long before the virgin forest has been exhausted. The fast-growing towns commit terrible aggression upon them.

The nutlike seed of the Paraná pine is the largest and most delicious of all the edible conifer seeds. It is as large as a chestnut and is gathered by the natives and Italian settlers, who boil them, for they make an excellent food. They are common in the markets of the cities of Southern Brazil.

The total forest area of Brazil, a country of over 3,000,000 square miles, is reputed to be 1,395,000 square miles, or 24.7 per cent of the total land area. Only 155,000 square miles consists of conifers and the great majority is tropical rain forest. The country, which is the largest state of South America, lies almost wholly within the tropics and is still in great part unexplored and unsettled. The warm south equatorial currents sweep the coast and pass up through the Caribbean Sea into the Gulf of Mexico. These, the greatest tropical forests in the world, are drained by the mighty Amazon and its tributaries. There are large areas of flood plains and swamps, heavily wooded and only sparsely inhabited by Indians. But Brazil really possesses three great river systems, for there are large areas drained by the Plata and São Francisco. The Amazon and its tributaries drain fully half of the country. To the east of the Madeira, these tributaries are tableland rivers, broken by rapids and only navigable for comparatively short distances. West of the Madeira they are lowland rivers, sluggish, bordered by extensive flood plains and navigable for long distances. The La Plata system drains nearly one fifth of the country through its three branches, the Paraguay, Paraná, and Uruguay. The first of these is a lowland river easily navigated for a long distance, while the other two are tableland rivers, full of obstructions and without free outlets for their upper level navigation. The São Francisco is a tableland river, flowing northeast between the Goyaz and maritime mountains, and then breaking through the latter, southeast to the Atlantic. Its tributaries are comparatively short, and nearly disappear along the lower river in the region of slight rainfall. It is not freely navigated because of the Paulo Offonso Falls. The other coast rivers are generally short.

The climate of Brazil has great variations, the lowlands of the Amazon and the major part of the coast being hot, humid, and unhealthy, while the tablelands and some districts of the coast, swept by the trade winds, are temperate and healthy. There are large areas subject to serious droughts, but for the greater part the vegetation of Brazil and Amazonia proper is luxuriant and varied. The vast rain forests of the Amazon contain hundreds of species of trees draped and festooned by climbing plants and orchids, and yield many beautiful and attractive woods. Rosewood was familiar as a decorative wood throughout the last century. Its popularity began with the Empire Period and in the early days of Queen Victoria's reign, used both solid and in veneer, it was employed in the best cabinet work. The Bahia timber stood first for quality, while that from Rio, though less well marked and figured, produced both larger and better pieces free from defect. It has remained in favor more in France and America than in the United Kingdom; this may have been partly due to the difficulty experienced in obtaining good, sound wood of a sufficiently large size to yield good veneer or panels. The peroba-rosa, *Aspidosperma peroba,* is of a pale rose color with some darker streaks. It has a very hard, firm, close-grained texture. In appearance it resembles the East African pencil cedar, but is very much harder. Zebrawood, *Astronium fraxinifolium,* is, as its name implies, characteristically striped. Brazilwood, *Caesalpinia echinata,* is of a rich bright-red color and is mostly used as a dye wood, while the best pieces are selected for turning and for violin bows. It is outstandingly the best wood for this last purpose, and, although many different kinds of timber have been tried, there is nothing that will yield the same result as the *Pernambuco* or Brazilwood, and many players will use no other kind on account of the peculiarly strong resilient spring only to be found in this wood. When planed, it has a bright metallic, lustrous surface and shows fine, snakelike ripple marks. Santa maria, *Calophyllum brasiliense,* is pale reddish in color, is moderately hard, has a fine straight grain, is easily worked, and is sometimes used in place of mahogany. Kingwood, *Dalbergia sp.,* is of a rich violet-brown, shading sometimes almost to black, and streaked with varying lighter and darker markings of golden-yellow. It has a bright luster and will finish with a smooth surface. It is always beautiful as a cabinet wood, and as it tones with age its value is greatly enhanced. Brazilian tulip wood, *Physocalymma scaberrimum,* is fresh red in color, streaked with deeper red and light yellow stripes. It is dense and hard and very liable to split after being sawn, but it is a favorite wood in the composition of French pieces of furniture, especially of the Empire Period, and is still used for bandings and ornamental inlay work. Peroba branca, *Paratecoma peroba,* is light grayish-yellow in color. It attains large dimensions and is fit for use in architecture, for furniture, and generally in the domestic arts. The tree is of straight growth and is even stronger than teak, *Tectona grandis.* At one time Brazilian ironclads were built of it. It is a valuable timber and should find many important uses. Quebracho, *Schinopsis lorentzii,* is one of the best-known woods both in Brazil and in the Argentine. It is very hard and heavy and is exceedingly dense, with close grain and a deep red color. It is principally used for railway ties, immense quantities of which are exported. It is also felled to a great extent for the manufacture of charcoal. Swietenia is one of the *Meliaceae,* which might be termed the mahogany family. The swietenia trees themselves have leaves which recall those of an ash in design though not in shape. It is not only one of the most important furniture woods, but is used for pattern making, and many key industries depend upon ample supplies of this wood. Because of its decorative qualities, it is very much sought after in furniture making and has a unique reputation on account of its beautiful grain and markings.

Besides producing valuable timber, the great forest of the

Amazon also yields rubber, and the well-known Pará is the
native home of the tree which is now grown so extensively in
plantations. The popular Brazilian nut is from a forest tree,
and great quantities are collected for export.

In supporting my proposal for a World Charter for Forestry
in 1946, Senhor Dr. J. J. Moniz de Aragão, Ambassador of
Brazil, said:

> I must confess to a certain diffidence in addressing you
> at this delightful ceremony of today, as my ignorance of
> forestry is—alas!—very great.
>
> In one respect, however, I appreciate the reason for
> having been invited to speak on the subject of trees.
>
> As you are no doubt aware, Brazil represents, today, by
> far the largest extent of forest of any country in the world.
> With the exception of a clearly defined area in the South
> of Brazil, where the araucaria or umbrella pine flourishes,
> all of this vast expanse is covered by hardwoods of the
> most varied kind. Contrary to most other timber areas,
> Brazilian hardwood forests enjoy the peculiarity of having
> no stands of timber of any *one* variety exclusively—but
> represent a veritable UNO of dozens of species living to-
> gether in perfect amity and security.
>
> Now this, although a grave disadvantage from the angle
> of economic exploitation, has this recompense as seen from
> the point of view of this Society, that the destruction of
> our forests is much less than it might otherwise have been,
> and, in fact, only occurs when land has to be cleared for
> the cultivation of coffee, cotton, sugar, or grain. This does
> not mean that many of our noble virgin forests have not
> been carelessly sacrificed, but it can be said, on the whole,
> that relatively small inroads have been made in the great
> kingdom of primeval forest, where life, as it existed in the
> dawn of history, still continues unchanged.
>
> How long this state of affairs can last is hard to say.
> Brazil is the fourth largest country in the world in extent,

with a population approximately that of the United Kingdom.

Owing to the political state of Europe, not only during the war, but for a considerable number of years before, immigration into Brazil was severely reduced. Now that hostilities have ceased, my country intends to embark on a vast scheme of developing our hinterland to a degree previously unknown. But no longer will immigration be uncontrolled, but scientifically planned.

This implies that wanton destruction of our great trees will not be permitted unchecked. Brazil will greatly benefit by this farsighted program, which, by sparing the trees wherever possible, will, above all, prevent land erosion, that inevitable fate of land laid waste by indiscriminate destruction of forests, and will prevent vast fertile areas of my country being transformed, as is the case in so many other lands, into a hopeless and sterile desert.

In Brazil, timber is extensively used as fuel on certain railways, for which, nearly always, second-growth trees are utilized. For the last twenty years it has been the practice of these railways to plant the land adjoining their tracks with vast extents of the eucalyptus tree, which has the advantage of growing with great rapidity and transforming mosquito-ridden swamps into healthy areas, and to utilize the timber at the end of ten years for fuel and for sleepers. I believe I am right in stating that these eucalyptus plantations in Brazil constitute the largest stands of this timber in the world.

With the rapidly expanding iron industry in the State of Minas Gerais, wood is at present being extensively transformed into charcoal for the reduction of our iron ore into pig-iron. Here, too, our Government have taken immediate steps for the reafforestation of lands thus denuded.

To conclude, I feel pride in being able to say that my country is fully alive to the ideals and precepts of this

Society, to the benefits of mankind in general, the importance of which cannot be too strongly stressed in any land
thus favored by nature. To its dyewoods Brazil owes its
very name.

The Spanish republic of Peru, with a coastline of 1400 miles
along the Pacific, has an area of 522,700 square miles with a
total forest area of 270,000 square miles, or 51.6 per cent of the
total land area. The Montaña is the region of tropical forest
within the basin of the River Amazon, including the wooded
slopes of the eastern watershed of the Andes, which may be
called the subtropical portion of the Montaña. This is the
region of the coca, *Erythroxylon coca,* from which cocaine is
made. I have found the bush growing on plains in the Highlands of Kenya. My carriers would sometimes chew the leaf
when they were fatigued on a long *safari* and they found it
mildly stimulating. From the forest-covered plains come India
rubber, sarsaparilla, the Peruvian mahogany, and a great
variety of useful and ornamental timber. The Sierra of Peru is
the original home of the potato. Its lofty heights also produce
several other edible roots and the grain called "quinoa," while
splendid crops of maize are grown in the valleys. Early agriculture in Peru was particularly notable for the remarkable
systems of terraces that it produced. As soon as the forest land
was cleared for cultivation, it was found necessary to throw
up small earth barriers to catch the soil washed down from
above and each year, as more soil came down, the barriers had
to be raised and lengthened until in the course of centuries a
complete terrace system came into existence. This ancient system might, in many of the newer countries where forest clearing is taking place, be supplemented by a pattern of protective
tree belts, including leguminous species which, while fixing the
soil with its root system, would at the same time impregnate
the ground with nitrogen.

Ecuador may be regarded as consisting of three divisions:
the lowlands west of the Andes, the mountainous plateau of the
interior, and the less elevated country to the east. Where the

rain clouds of the Pacific are caught, the gorges of the western spurs of mountains and most of the land are covered with luxurious tropical vegetation. Valuable trees and plants wage bloodless conflict in a battle of species for existence against the stifling embraces of creepers, mosses, parasitic plants, and gorgeous orchids. Of the total land area of 167,600 square miles, 90,000 square miles, or 53.6 per cent, is forest. The world was first indebted to the province of Loja for cinchona bark, from which quinine is made.

The great Republic of Colombia, occupying the northwest corner of the South American Continent from the frontiers of Ecuador, Peru, Brazil, and Venezuela to those of Panama, with 500 miles of coast on the Caribbean Sea and 600 on the Pacific, has a land area estimated at 462,000 square miles, of which 231,000 square miles—fifty per cent of the total land area of the country—is classed as forest.

Addressing the World Forestry Charter Luncheon, Señor Don Arturo Martinez Herrera, Colombian Embassy, said:

I am here today as a mere substitute, circumstances beyond his control having prevented our ambassador from being present at this gathering. The few remarks I am about to make have, however, been the subject of conversations between us.

We share to the full your conviction that the problem of food shortages, which now confronts the world and threatens to become permanent, needs something more than the creation of UNRRA and moral exhortations and that in no other field of human activity is co-operation so necessary.

It is therefore with a deep sense of our responsibilities towards this movement that we join you today.

We in Colombia are confronted with a problem which, in the present state of our financial and technical resources, seems beyond our strength. Lack of statistics and the absence of periodical surveys have for a long time veiled the threatening devastation of our lands. But we are feeling the full blast of the drought that from our bare mountains and nude valleys is sweeping away our agriculture. We learn how, in one of our countries alone, 200 hectares of arable land are daily washed away by our father river on its way to the sea; how the river which provides water for one of our largest cities has been reduced to a third of its volume in the last ten years; how injudicious colonization has led to the deforestation of the heads of our rivers, in order to bring the land under cultivation. In one specific case we have spent considerable sums during the last seven years to reforest the head of a river which provides the water supply of another important city and irrigates one of our richest valleys, besides providing a waterway through which trade and commerce have flowed in the past. And additional expenditure has been necessary for resettling in more suitable areas the people who were unwisely allowed to settle in such vital places.

I think that, bearing in mind our experience and the waste understandable in such vast areas, our legislation, if not altogether effective, now aims at stemming the speed of the destruction. A law passed in 1938 makes it compulsory for each landowner to plant for every hectare [1 hectare = 2.4711 acres] in his possession, ten trees whose wood may be used for building purposes. The same law establishes that whenever new land is granted, trees may be felled for the use of their timber, but each tree felled must be replaced with one of its own kind. We have in every county town or city with a revenue of over 1,000,-000 pesos a special tax known as "the park and tree tax," the amounts collected to be applied to the building and improvement of parks (especially children's parks) and the planting of trees in squares, streets, and roads. And the majority of our cities offer a beautiful spectacle of streets, even those congested with traffic being lined throughout their length with lovely trees.

You will understand, of course, that in a country such

as ours, with great expanses of unoccupied lands, sparse population, and poor technical means, it is a very difficult task indeed to protect our forests and to enforce existing legislation.

Our men and women have begun to realize, however, the magnitude of the problem and the tree has been recognized again as a faithful and useful friend. There is a sort of reconciliation between man and forest. The character of our forests is no longer, as Aldous Huxley said, appalling, or fundamentally and utterly inimical to intruding man. Nor is, as he adds, "the life of those vast masses of swarming vegetation alien to the human spirit and hostile to it."

Of course many years will pass and more good earth will be lost before we achieve the reafforestation scheme of the Scottish Highlands or our schools provide millions of trees, as in Australia. Our problem is great, but no problem is beyond human ingenuity and human co-operation, and we welcome this opportunity to draw on the common pool of knowledge provided by this association.

We look to you for guidance on common principles and common measures. Show us what you have done; enlighten us with your experience; advise us in our technical difficulties, so that we may all go forward together in a great cause.

The United States of Venezuela has a total land area of 398,600 square miles, almost half of which is forest. It is a land of mountains and valleys in the west and north, of lower mountains and wooded hills in the south, of llanos between the Orinoco and the northern ranges, and of lake, swamp, and forest in the northwest. The llanos occupy a quarter of the country lying between the Orinoco and northern chains, and are mostly undulating plains of long grass, broken by low plateaus or mesas and by numerous clumps of trees and belts of forest which rise out of the savanna. The llanos north of the lower Orinoco towards Paria Peninsula are dreary, sand-swept, and treeless, except along the shallow water courses. Vegetation in the Tierra Caliente is luxuriant beyond description. The forests are dense with noble trees, and yield gums, balsams, dyewoods, India rubber, sarsaparilla, quinine, vanilla, and tanka beans. Where water fails in the low-lying valleys, cactus forms take the place of other vegetation.

Partridge wood, *Caesalpinia granadillo,* formerly often employed in the Brazils for shipbuilding, is known in British dockyards as cabbage wood and is now principally used for walking sticks, or umbrella and parasol sticks, and in cabinet work and turning. The wood is close, heavy, and generally straight in the grain.

The Venezuelan boxwood is famous; it is beautifully grown, and attains a height of 70 feet, practically free from a single knot throughout its length. At the extreme top the tree branches out into a tuft of foliage. Besides being used for inlay work and banding in cabinets, for handles of all kinds of tools, for brush backs, mathematical instruments and rules, barometer backs, and for many kinds of turned work, in France and Germany it is now extensively employed for making small combs.

British Guiana is the home of the famous greenheart, *Ocotea rodiaei,* from which salmon, trout, and other fishing rods are made. A fine sample of greenheart can be made into an exceedingly small top joint for such a rod, and will bend to an extraordinary extent without breaking. The color is of a pale yellowish-green, while sometimes it is quite dark with brown and black streaks. The black greenheart is considered to be the best. It is largely used for piles for sea jetties and docks; although not entirely immune, the wood is partially proof against the attack of the teredo worm.

The total forest area of British Guiana is 78,700 square miles, or eighty-eight per cent of the total land area. That of Dutch Guiana is 48,000 square miles, or ninety per cent, and that of French Guiana 24,000 square miles, or seventy per cent. One of the best-known timbers from French Guiana is angélique, *Dicorynia paraensis.* The wood is of a reddish-brown color, clean and even in the grain, moderately hard, tough, strong, elastic, and not difficult to work, although it does not cleave readily. It has been said that it does not rot in water, that it is durable, and that it is proof against attacks from many insects to which other timber is prone. The mora wood, *Mora excelsa,* is found both in British and in Dutch Guiana. My old Reader in Forestry, Herbert Stone, used to say that it is more durable than teak. He recognized three varieties: the red, the white, and mora-bucquia; this last, however, is not considered to be durable. The wood of mora proper is a yellowish-brown color and contains in its pores an oily and glutinous substance which probably contributes to its durability. It is of close texture, and has occasionally a twist or waviness in the fiber which imparts to the logs possessing it a beautifully figured appearance. In its native forest it stands out conspicuously among the other trees. Sometimes an old tree may be seen festooned with creepers, the wild fig tree often rears itself from one of the thick branches at its top, and when its fruit is ripe the birds will resort to it for nourishment. An undigested seed, passing through the body of a bird which had perched on the mora, grew to the fig tree which found itself in this elevated position. The sap of the mora tree nourished it, and in time maybe it would itself become host to other species of vines. Such creepers soon vegetate and bear fruit, and in their turn attract other birds, who deposit further seeds—and so the old mora tree becomes an unwilling host to numbers of parasitic creepers which trail themselves along his branches and intertwine him with neighboring trees. Such is life in the Guiana forests. A vine which the woodcutters call "the bush rope," on account of its use in hauling out the heaviest timber, is conspicuous in the forests of Demerara. Sometimes it may be seen almost as thick as a man's body, twisting itself like a corkscrew around the tallest tree and rearing its head high above the top of its host. These vines will sometimes throw out aerial roots which in time reach the ground and pass on or entangle other trees, joining tree and tree and branch and branch together. Other parasitic creepers will throw out shoots in all directions, forming a veritable mat of tangled lianas. Often a tree uprooted by a whirlwind will be caught in the cat's cradle thus formed and be held for years 'twixt earth and sky. It may take a new lease on life and throw up fresh shoots at the junction of root and 'trunk, while all along the sloping trunk will appear fresh shoots, which in their turn grow erect in their search for light. It is said that the topmost branch of an old dead mora tree, when naked with age or struck by lightning, is the favorite resort of the toucan, where he sits yelping far out of range of the gun of the fowler. He is a deep-forest bird, feeding on the fruits and seeds of the forest, his mate laying eggs in hollow trees, which he serves by helping to distribute their seeds for regeneration. Many other birds play their part in helping to perpetuate the remarkable forests of this great hemisphere.

It is devoutly to be wished that the comparatively extensive tree cover of South America will be preserved, for it is a unique possession in our world of ruthless exploitation of woodland wealth and should be maintained in the interest of the human race. Speaking broadly, it has never happened in history that sylvan economy has been maintained. The story of the rise and fall of past civilizations has coincided with the exploitation of the forests—each rose to their peak, then declined as green forest mantle was lost. Unaware of their dependence upon trees, they failed to preserve a reasonable soil cover, and so exposed their society to the fall which must come as the result of such ignorant negligence. The world is slow to recognize the need for great forests close to large centers of population. Legislation seems powerless to guarantee protection or ensure the future existence of the human race. It would seem that nothing short of a universal spiritual regeneration will suffice to change the heart of man and enable him to recognize the law of return and the reasonable demands made by the Creator.

20.

TREES OR FAMINE

THE STORY of the forests of the world is an endless one and it is quite impossible to tell it in a single volume. It begins long before man existed on this planet, and it will end only if man fails to recognize his dependence upon tree growth for his existence. The fundamental history of civilization is the history of the soil and its cover. Civilization is a race between education and catastrophe. We have traveled far in our survey and have already witnessed the disastrous effects which follow the removal of the essential covering. We have seen that it is possible to conserve and replenish the forests of the world and maintain an adequate standard of living in all countries, provided people unite in this task. The earth is a great entail, and it belongs as much to those who come after as to ourselves.

Traveling up from the South American Continent, we glimpse the equatorial and tropical forest regions of Central America, where Aztec and earlier civilizations left stone sculpture and monumental remains now covered in the dark recesses of tropic bush.

Costa Rica, the most southerly of the five older republics of Central America, with its total land area of 23,000 square miles, is said to contain 10,000 square miles of forest. On the Atlantic slope, dense forests prevail, but wide savannas are more frequent on the Pacific side. Besides valuable timber and dyewoods, it yields coffee, and 10 million bunches of bananas are exported or have been exported in a single year. The banana crop is very exacting on the soil, and much of the old banana land should be returned to forest if exhaustion is to be prevented.

Nicaragua, with an area of 51,700 square miles, has a forest area of 25,000 square miles. The history of the country after the severance from Spain is a record of war and dissension, and although she has made laudable efforts to develop her resources, all too little has been done to perpetuate her forests on scientific lines.

Salvador, the smallest but most thickly populated of the Central American Republics, consists of a strip of territory stretching between Honduras and the Pacific, and is bounded on the west by Guatemala and on the east by Fonesca Bay, which separates it from Nicaragua. With a total land area of 13,200 square miles, she possesses a forest area of only 1200 square miles.

For many years famous for its mahogany, Honduras still retains virgin forests of considerable size, amounting to 6640 square miles, which have covered the ancient civilization of the Mayas.

In the uplands of Guatemala are forests of huge pine, spruce, and oak. Altogether they contain over 100 kinds of timber trees, including many of the most valuable. Today the Mayan peoples retain only legends of their former greatness.

Cuba is the largest island of the West Indies, being 759 miles in length from Cape Maysi on the east to Cape Antonio on the west, with a breadth varying from twenty-seven to ninety miles and an area of 43,000 square miles, in addition to which there are 2000 miles of rocks and islets, including the island of Pinos, making a total of 45,000 square miles. The forest area has been estimated at 7000 square miles, only one per cent of which is virgin. The high mountains produce woods suitable for sawing and have been heavily exploited, along with the forests of the low mountains, which today only provide firewood, charcoal, and other products of small dimension. For many years the forests of Cuba produced the well-known swietenia mahogany and other valuable woods. The famous Mexican cigar-box cedar, *Cedrela Mexicana,* known locally as *cedre,* is much in demand, as well as the wood of three pines known locally as the male pine tree (*Pinus caribea*), the female pine (*Pinus tropicalis*), and the Baracoa pine (*Pinus occidentalis*). No method of reafforestation has been employed, although a few experimental woods have been planted. Selection is the method employed in using the products of the high mountains, but complete cutting takes place in the lower mountains. The Cuban forests have suffered ill effects from World War II, for the extraction of woods of all kinds has been much increased. Many areas have been entirely devastated and cut for agricultural purposes. The value of the products taken from the forests in 1944 amounted to over twelve million dollars.

Señor Don Julio A. Brodermann, Cuban Consul General, speaking on the occasion of the second gathering in London held to further a World Charter for Forestry, said:

> On behalf of the Cuban legation in London I had the privilege last time we met to support the movement in favor of the preservation and increase of the forest resources of the world, which means in all countries where lands are available for planting trees, or forests exist.
>
> I am glad to have the opportunity again to support this movement on behalf of the Cuban Government, who take great interest in this matter. Forests and trees are one of the important sources of wealth of Cuba and the Government is taking suitable measures to increase and conserve the forest resources of the island.
>
> This organization, which is doing such excellent work, deserves the support of all governments and of the people everywhere, and I think we can count on their co-operation in preparing a World Charter for Forestry and in carrying out the program which that charter will provide.

I can assure you of the good will of Cuba in this useful enterprise.

The mountainous country of Haiti is, after Cuba, the largest of the West Indian islands. It has a total area of 11,000 square miles, 5700 square miles of which is forest.

Santo Domingo is the principal source of lignum vitae, *Guaiacum officinale,* one of the hardest and heaviest woods in the world and one of the most useful of timbers; for a great many purposes it has been found impossible to produce a substitute. The maintenance of a sufficient supply may indeed be said to be a question of world importance. There is nothing equal to it for the making of sheaves for blocks, and when employed in this way it wears well and seems almost imperishable. Perhaps the most important of the many uses to which it is put is the bushing of the stern tubes for propeller shafts in even the largest ships. Owing to the silky nature of the wood and the oil contained in it, acting in conjunction with the water, a natural lubricant is formed. The life of the material when used in this manner is extraordinary and varies from three to seven years, the shortest period being the life of the wood for a fast ship like the *Queen Elizabeth.* It is also used for the packing between saws in machine-saw frames.

Jamaica, or the Land of Springs, the largest and most important of the British West Indies, has little forest left, although the island is transversed from east to west by a range of mountains which are the natural domain of trees and forest. The virgin woods have almost disappeared, yet there are still many valuable trees, such as balata or beef-wood, *Mimusops globosa,* mahogany, logwood, lignum vitae, fustic, ebony, and satinwood. A farsighted policy would allow for protective forest belts following the contours of the mountains and providing shelter for the famous Blue Mountain coffee and the many other valuable agricultural crops.

Mexico, with a total area of 760,000 square miles, has about 20 billion cubic feet of pines in her mountain forests at a range of from 7000 to 10,000 feet and so far these reserves have not suffered, because the means of extracting timber has been by oxcart or by mule over poor trails, in a primitive, hand-lumbering way. But those forests will inevitably disappear when modern lumbering tackle is used. In the lowlands, dyewoods and valuable timber abound. Speaking at the World Forestry Charter Luncheon held in London in April, 1945, Señor Dr. Don Alfonso de R. Diaz, the Mexican Ambassador to the Court of St. James, fully endorsed my proposals for the formation of a World Forestry Committee and the preparation of a World Charter for Forestry. He has planted trees, and trees are his hobby. Wandering in many parts of the world, he has devoted time to admiring the most outstanding trees of each country. He recalled in Mexico the famous tree of Tacuba, beneath whose branches the conqueror Hernán Cortés wept; also the tree of Santa Maria del Tule in the State of Oaxaca, with a girth so great that it took thirty men to encircle it; and finally "The Soldado," a millenary tree of the world-unique Chapultepec Forest. In Venezuela he went to see near Macaray the tree called "Mato-Palo," beneath whose branches Simon Bolivar and his troops stayed for rest and shade during his wonderful campaigns. In Central America he saw the La Ceiba national tree, the design of which appeared on the coins in that part of the world, with the inscription *Libre crezca Fecundo.* In El Salvador he stood awed by the balsamic tree, and in Sweden it was his pleasure to walk round the forests thinking that trees can also be civilized.

"And now I give a call to you," the ambassador said, "an idea that will surely result in many trees being planted. I propose that we promote the publication of a monumental work dedicated to the tree, which shall contain plates of the most outstanding trees of the world. A committee might be appointed to study this question and the possibility of its being put into practice under the patronage of the ministers of agriculture of the United Nations."

This present work is a first attempt to create what the Mexican Ambassador had in mind, leading on to the deeper significance which trees hold for mankind.

When the North American Continent was first opened up, trees were felled in large numbers and the virgin soil cleared for exploitation by the new settlers. In many areas this soil was very rich and afforded heavy wheat crops year after year without much care. Many of the early settlers did not trouble at all to replenish or nourish the soil, but moved farther on to fresh virgin soil when the first farm showed signs of depletion. But even farmers trained in England have confessed that they saw the soil simply vanish under their feet in the course of a lifetime of farming in America. It seems hardly credible that a man could learn farming in England, emigrate to America, deplete a number of feet of virgin soil, and return to England to farm again. That would mean destroying soil at the rate of about one inch a year, and it takes about 400 years to build up one inch of good soil under favorable conditions.

The process is relatively simple. Here was a chance of making money. The timber that was felled brought a good return, which enabled the settler to build his home and gather about him a certain amount of equipment. Good harvests of grain followed year after year, without the necessity of putting much back into the gradually thinning soil. Heat, rain, and wind began to carry away the soil bodily. Deprived of its cover of leaf and blade, the soil was dried up by the summer sun and blown away in clouds of dust. Dust storms in some parts were so bad that they stopped operations in hospitals, because the dust could not be kept out of the operating theaters in the towns. Whole farms were carried away by the wind. Then on sloping ground the water, after rain, cut gullies in the soil or washed it away in sheets, so that the streams and rivers became silted up and the rivers had to overflow their normal banks. Thus the felling of timber in the uplands affected the surface of the earth as far down as the estuaries, or even the sea itself. The 1930's brought the record-breaking floods and dust storms. Practically all crop-growing vitality has been swept from nearly one seventh of the surface of the United States. Estimates based on the rapid rate of deterioration of the soil during this period were so alarming that it was considered likely that within 100 years the territory of the United States would afford a livelihood for but a few million people along the seaboard, and that the rest of the country would be reduced to irretrievable desert. In any case, it is known that erosion has made its mark upon 1000 million acres.

In years to come this profligate exploitation of land will no doubt be regarded as sheer madness, and yet to the people who were the actual cause of it—namely, the lumberers, farmers, and ranchers—it did not appear to be robbery and wastage of the national wealth. The fault lies chiefly in our manner of translating wealth into financial figures, and then manipulating the financial figures to estimate the play of social forces. Lumberers and farmers had to pay their way, and the more money they made, the greater was the social esteem in which they were held. Paying your way and making money were perhaps the greatest recognized virtues at the period which brought about the disaster in natural wealth. To the early settlers, it certainly never occurred that the time would come when maltreatment of soil would ever be noticeable in such a vast territory. To them the new land appeared utterly inexhaustible. But their example, followed by millions of successors, told a different story: the appalling one which is now familiar to us all.

The record-breaking floods and widespread dust storms of the 1930's dramatized the power of soil erosion, deepened economic depression, and intensified its effects upon the people. On all sides it became abundantly clear that conservation of the soil was a national necessity of the very highest order.

A nationwide soil-erosion control was launched for the first time in United States history and pushed forward along several fronts. Government technicians and Civilian Conservation Corps enrollees went into erosion-problem areas and helped farmers lay down defenses against rain and wind. Benefit payments were made available to all land operators who adopted specified soil-saving practices. State laws were passed giving farmers the power to form local co-operative societies for soil and water conservation.

In this many-sided movement, the Soil Conservation Service has played and is playing a major role. Through a program of research and farmland demonstrations, the Service has developed and improved practical measures of erosion control. The specific land treatments used and recommended by the Service vary from one valley to the next, from farm to farm, and even from field to field. Before any work is done, each farm or ranch is analyzed both as a piece of land and as a business enterprise.

In making the physical analysis, fieldmen of the Soil Conservation Service carefully note the lie of the land, the qualities of the soil, and the erosion hazards on every acre. As accurately as possible, they determine which lands can be cultivated under rotation practices without excessive soil loss, which lands need the protection afforded by special crop arrangements or special tillage practices, and which ones require a permanent safeguarding cover of trees or grass.

The next step in soil conservation is to work out a new farm layout based on the survey information. Steep or unproductive croplands, for example, may be earmarked for permanent cover of grass or trees; farm forests may be planned where grass is not paying, or where it is failing to hold the soil; gullied areas may be turned into grass-covered waterways or small-scale sanctuaries for animals and birds. The end in view is a new arrangement of fields, pastures, meadows, and woods that guards the soil and fits the land as Nature made it.

In many cases, this new layout may not entirely fit the farmer's pocketbook. It may call for more hay crops than he actually needs, and not enough cotton or corn; it may involve other changes that he simply cannot afford to make. If so, it is not a good layout in the final sense of the word, and it must be adjusted to family needs and market opportunities. Purely from the conservation standpoint, however, the layout based on physical land analysis is ideal. The closer the farmer can approach it and still make a living, the more stable and productive his land will be over the long run of years.

Drawing up a satisfactory land-use layout is only half the

job of planning for erosion control on the farm. Each parcel of land, even under the new use, generally needs some special practices or treatments for adequate soil protection. Croplands are nearly always farmed in rotation, usually on the level, and sometimes in strips; terraces are frequently built for added protection. Pastures are limed, fertilized, and grazed with caution to improve the growth of soil-guarding grass. Woodlands are fenced to keep out livestock, protected from fire, and managed according to scientific principles of forestry. These are only a few of the dozens of erosion-control practices that may be called into play. The new layout, *plus* the practices, makes up a complete farm plan for soil and water conservation. Under such a plan, soil conservation is not just an incidental farming activity; it becomes part and parcel of the whole business of making a living from the land.

Trees are one of Nature's most efficient weapons of soil defense. Conservation farmers use them to tie down steep hillsides, to check the growth of big gullies, to stabilize unsteady stream banks, and to screen off cultivated fields from harmful winds. At the same time trees also help to keep money in the family pocketbook, for they provide fuel for the home, posts for fences, timber for repairing barns and sheds, and saw logs for sale in the near-by markets. The ultimate goal of the Soil Conservation Service is a comprehensive inventory of the country's soil potentialities, an inventory that will aid farmers and farmer groups as well as local, state, and federal agencies in charting a safe and intelligent course for American agriculture.

It is a tragedy that in a country of 3,026,800 square miles there remains only an area of 284,000 square miles of exploitable forest. The people of the United States are eating into their forest capital at four and a half times the rate of the annual wood increment. They have cut seven eights of their virgin forests. Against that they have a secondary crop coming on in many parts where it was cut, but there have been colossal fires which have taken their toll. For many years the United States has had to resort to Canada for supplies of timber for pulp wood. Newsprint represents only about thirteen per cent of the total amount of woodpulp used; thirty per cent, for instance, is used as kraft or wrapping paper, and almost every day finds a new use for forest products in one form or another.

The development of the Dominion of Canada has been made possible by its extensive waterways and railway systems and, conversely, the natural resources of Canada have made their development possible. The boasted inexhaustibility of Canada's forests is a concept which should be used guardedly. Canada, like other countries rich in forest resources, has been extravagant and careless, though there are many hopeful signs that progressive forest protection measures in their broadest sense have advanced from theory to practice. There is still, however, a long hard road ahead. Forest protection in all its branches—against fire, disease, insects—is greater today than ever before. As Canada matures, the importance of scientific conservation and utilization is assuming its rightful place in the Dominion's economy and progress. The matter must not be brought to public attention only: it must be kept alive and advanced by sound legislation and education. Forest conservation is primarily education. Much may be learned from the experience of others, but our own experiences are, and will be, our best teacher. The law of itself does not put out forest fires. The only policeman worth while in our woods is the man who polices himself.

Canada, together with Newfoundland and Labrador, has a total area of 3,629,250 square miles, of which 1,290,960 square miles are forest, but only 810,000 square miles are classed as being of productive quality.

In Eastern Canada the principal softwood species are spruces: red, white, and jackpine; balsam fir, hemlock, and cedar. The most important hardwoods are maple, birch, and poplar. On the West Coast, the chief species are Douglas fir, Western hemlock, and Western red cedar, and these are accompanied by smaller quantities of pine, Sitka spruce, and true fir. In general, natural regeneration is relied upon throughout the forests, but about 20,000 acres have been planted annually. The total area of forests controlled by the Crown is 1,190,785 square miles, including both productive and unproductive forest areas. More than nine tenths of all the forests in Canada belong to the public and are known as Crown Forests. They are managed by governments on behalf of the people. Forests in the Northwest and Yukon Territories, and those in National Parks and Forest Experiment Stations, are controlled by the Federal Government, but all other Crown Forests are administered by the governments of the provinces in which they stand. Several provinces, notably Quebec, Ontario, and British Columbia, maintain large forest nurseries where planting stock is grown both for forest plantings and for the supply of farmers. Permanent nursery stations are maintained. Permanent staffs are small, but considerable local employment is provided during the transplanting seasons. The output of these stations runs into millions of small trees annually.

Accessible, merchantable saw timber is estimated at 60 billion cubic feet, and pulpwood at 50 billions. The forests are being exploited two and a half times as fast as the wood increment. Canada has about enough to last twenty-five years at the present rate of cutting or destruction. She is using about three fifths of the lumber she produces, and as her population grows her timber requirements may be expected to increase also. Dominion foresters are expressing grave concern over the situation. Fortunately, sweeping changes in forestry laws are now being made. In this matter, the move is coming from the Far West and, when it meets again in the near future, the Provincial Legislature will hear proposals for sweeping changes in statutes relating to British Columbia's leading source of revenue, its vast forest industry. The Government, which last spring began a step-by-step implementation of the Sloan Commission's recommendations, by appropriating an extra $1,000,000 for forest-fire protection, will go much further in the next phase of its forest plan, bringing down legislation that is likely to rate as the most important and far-reaching of the session's work.

With strong emphasis on reafforestation, it is believed the new measures to be introduced will be directed toward placing the entire industry on a sustained-yield basis—strongly advocated by Chief Justice Gordon Sloan.

The exact nature of the Government's proposals has not been disclosed, but it is understood that the new policy will embrace provisions to ensure reafforestation of logged-off lands, regulation of logging methods to prevent destructive exploitation, and revision of taxation and tenure system, to encourage private forestry and remove causes compelling liquidation.

Forest Department officials already are working on the first draft of the proposed legislation, closely following the recommendations of Chief Justice Sloan, who, in his report as Royal Commissioner, said:

> The present policy of unmanaged liquidation of our forest wealth must give way to the important concept of a planned forest policy designed to maintain our forests upon the principle of sustained yield production. Our forest land must be regarded as a source of renewable crops, and not as a mine to be exploited and abandoned.

The Canadian National railway system, with its 22,000 miles of active trackage, some 1840 miles of which are in the United States and the balance in Canada, needs some 60 million railway cross-ties or sleepers to carry the steel rails. The average yearly purchase of cross-ties is about 8 million. About ninety-three per cent of these are softwoods, seven per cent hardwoods. Although fires caused by locomotives have shown a marked decrease, owing largely to mechanical improvements and the use of better-grade coal, they still levy their toll on the forests. The Canadian National railways maintain twenty-five fire-fighting tank cars, varying in capacity from 3000 to 13,000 gallons, equipped with steam- and petrol-power pumps. These are stationed at strategic points along the railway and are kept in readiness during the fire season. Some 14,000 miles of territory are classified as forested, and on this mileage special patrol or attention is provided. But railway engines are not the only cause of forest fires, which annually devastate hundreds of thousands of acres. The careless tourist is responsible for many an outbreak. One tree will make a million matches, but one match, carelessly thrown away, may destroy a million trees.

Farm woodlots are making a valuable contribution toward the forest resources and are already contributing a large proportion of wood for all purposes. They are privately owned, and well-managed farm plantations are increasing the prosperity of the agricultural communities. Disease control is carried on in close collaboration with the Department of Agriculture, which maintains two tree-planting stations at Indian Head and Sutherland, Saskatchewan. These stations provide planting stock, for the establishment of windbreaks and shelter belts, to farmers in the three prairie provinces.

The Romans did not conquer Britons by force of arms, for the forests protected them; it was not until the country was bribed to export wheat to feed the people of Rome that the forests were seriously invaded and destroyed to provide the land to grow wheat to make money. In spite of the Romans, the core of England remained primeval forest.

Down through the ages, the forests of these favored islands have provided food and shelter. Despite the efforts of all her enemies to mar and scar the face of this green and pleasant land, the trees still function, though only as scattered woodlands, too often neglected. Even when destroyed, trees leave their traces on the face of the country, truthfully recording aggression by water, ice, or man. Their influence, too, remains and inspirits the very being of the people.

But there has been a growing demand for luxury, tending to turn men from a natural life and soften them in the process. A mere whim is handed down through the various strata until the mass of people claim it as their right. The pyramid becomes inverted and economic stability is threatened. The story of Britain is that of forest destruction. A few ancient yews still

remain as witnesses of the last 2000 years of English life. There
are a few oaks, too, *Quercus robur,* signs of original forest
trees, which would form an interesting biological study. The
few surviving giants of the forest are decrepit with age. The
ravages of man have left but a few survivors to deplore the process of urbanization and the reduction of the economic forest
area to but three per cent of the total area of the land. World
War I was the means of reducing Britain's forest by 800,000
acres, and World War II cost one million acres. Land alienated
today by the War Office for training purposes amounts to
another two million acres of ground. Besides the land sterilized
by the War Department, there are at least seven and a half
million idle acres below the standard of agriculture which
might well be dedicated to the growing of trees. Much of this
land consists of steep hillsides which urgently need forest
covering and which in the early days of colonization were
covered with virgin growth. Most of the forests have vanished,
and today Great Britain, with a land area of 80,000 square
miles, has a total forest covering of less than one sixteenth,
while only half of this can be regarded as forest of economic
value. English improvidence may be compared with that of
Spain and Italy in past centuries, and is only equaled by that
of the United States and Australia today. In the Ice Age the
forests of Britain were forced to retreat, but they were not
vanquished. Modern urbanization is a greater menace than
the glaciers of old.

21.

FOR THE HEALING OF THE NATIONS

THE HEALTH and the economic security of the human race depend on how well the forests of the world are managed. All the countries of the world are suffering the penalty resulting from man's neglect to plant where he has reaped. He has destroyed the gifts of a generous Creator without realizing that they were a trust to be handed on to future generations. The earth's green covering is Nature's capital, and, if man exacts more than the interest or annual increment, he is endangering the source of wealth and the very means of his existence on the planet.

The forest is the mother of the rivers and one of Nature's most important means of regulating and maintaining the flow and quality of water. How the forests are managed decides whether the rain and snow they receive will be a blessing or a catastrophe. Water is the priceless resource on which all growing things depend. It is the lifeblood of the earth. Where there are ample supplies of good water, vigorous nations can flourish, farms thrive, and cities prosper. When the supply of water fails, farms are abandoned, communities are impoverished, and cities and cultures die, leaving crumbling ruins to mark their transient glory.

History has shown that Nature exacts payment for her

abuse and disaster follows when man breaks the divine law of the universe. Earth is a sentient being and feels the behavior of the sons of men, whom she has nurtured upon her breast. Is it to be wondered that she is wilting under severe maltreatment? Man, in his dire folly, has removed vast areas of virgin forest, and now the end of earth's sylvan wealth is in sight. There is no time to be lost if man is to be saved from bringing disaster on this planet and himself.

Water is the source of life to a man dying of thirst, or a farm needing irrigation, but it can also be a deadly enemy to all life when uncontrolled by the essential forest covering. Urban water users and valley dwellers, though remote from the watershed forests, are bound to suffer the consequences of damaged uplands. All people should demand that reasonable tree cover be maintained, so that erosion and rapid run-off may be prevented; otherwise their health and well-being are imperiled. Every man, woman, and child is really under duress not to waste water, or use it without thought for Nature's own needs. As people learn more about the essential tree cover and appreciate the increasing value of forests for watershed protection, they will see to it that the forests are not maltreated. Forest fires, which are largely the result of carelessness or thoughtlessness, continue to do great damage, threatening to deplete and reduce the tree cover to a point at which it cannot adequately serve its function. By the prevention of forest fires, enormous annual losses to every interest and section of the community may be minimized. There should be adequate conservation laws in every country and governments should purchase suitable watershed, cutover, idle, and semi-arid lands for reafforestation under scientific forestry supervision. All means possible should be employed to encourage the planting of trees and the creation of forests to provide sufficient cover, so that an approximation to the natural circulation of water may be restored.

We believe that the great task of conserving and replenishing the forests of the world and reclaiming the deserts and waste places by tree planting requires the concerted action of every country, and at the same time provides a common meeting ground for all men. We believe that in order to save humanity we must save men, and in order to save the forests we must save the trees. To live our bodily life on this earth we must get food, clothes, and shelter. To do this we must take care of the earth beneath our feet and especially not meddle wantonly with the natural circulation of water, which meddling has been the cause of great loss of soil all over the globe. We must rightly return to the earth the waste of whatever we take from it. In saving the forests of the world, we accomplish all these ends. But as we look out on the world today we see that monster cities are tapping wider areas and the water table is sinking in all areas of civilization. A halt must be called; otherwise the means of life will vanish. It is not our aim to clothe the surface of the earth with an unbroken forest cover, but rather to see to it that every city has its catchment area and every farm and hamlet its protecting trees. We visualize valley settlement as the cradle of sound culture. Food is the first necessity of a healthy, industrious, and happy life. It will be a whole life, balanced in every respect, in which well-being is not necessarily the result of financial success, but the outcome of work well done without thought of personal gain; each and all working together for the good of the whole. The accomplishment of this purpose will assure not only the perpetuation of the forests through intelligent use, and the preservation of real wealth in growing trees and forests, but the regeneration of the very spirit of man, for in this life he may find the highest and the best.

World afforestation is necessary because it is the most constructive and peaceable enterprise in which the nations could co-operate. It would check, stop, and reverse the advance of the deserts upon the good lands of the globe, and thus relieve the growing shortage of foods. If food sources are allowed to become more restricted than they are at present, the tendency to grab unlawfully for them will increase intolerably, thus making for war with its large-scale destruction; whereas, if genuine co-operation can be rallied internationally for the purpose of preserving and increasing the primary producing areas of the land surface, the tendency will be toward peace and future prosperity.

With the object of furthering such international co-operation, the Society of the Men of the Trees has sponsored gatherings in London for representatives of the Diplomatic Corps. Those attending included officials from twenty-four countries, and the resolution placed before the last gathering by the chairman, the Right Honorable Lord Sempill, was passed unanimously for transmission to the United Nations Organization:

> That realizing in face of the present world famine the dependence of man on trees and forests and seeing the forests disappearing and the deserts encroaching on the remaining food sources at a rate of up to thirty miles per year on 1000-mile fronts in three continents, this gathering of national representatives of twenty-four countries request the aid of the United Nations Organization in the preparation of a WORLD CHARTER FOR FORESTRY.

The United Nations Organization has taken the matter up in response to the World Forestry Committee's resolution, and its investigating section accepted from us a few directions for eventual recommendation to all member nations of the United Nations. We are well aware that it may be a long way from this stage of investigation to the time when reafforestation becomes a first priority in world undertakings. But the start we have made is encouraging, and we shall no doubt advance rapidly because we have Nature herself to back us. The nations of the world and not merely their experts and political leaders are gradually waking to the consciousness that the shortage of food and other primary products may not cure itself with inertia and time. We say *may* not, because it is possible that, by removing human interference and taking the job on herself, Nature could restore the cover of the earth with inertia and time. This is a very important point, as it is suggested by some experts that outworked territories should be sealed off and left to the healing work of Nature, instead of being replanted with trees, as we urge. But if the cure is left to Nature, it is most likely that the disturbers—that is to say, we human beings—may be thinned out very thoroughly to facilitate the cure of earth's distress. The means of thinning us out is temptingly handy in present political friction and scientific instruments of modern warfare.

We have already advanced to the United Nations the suggestion that the minimum of safety in tree cover is ten per cent of the habitable land area. Therefore, the first step we urge toward the restoration of balance is tree planting up to ten per cent of every catchment area of every state subscribing to the policy of world afforestation.

The next step we advocate is the formation of a faculty or university of land reclamation, a world center where this all-important problem may be studied and at the same time put into practice. Such a body might be founded in the foothills of the Atlas Mountains of North Africa, surrounded by land which in course of time has been exploited and become unproductive. This center would welcome research students and members of forestry and farming faculties elected from universities and schools from every nation. It might be called the University of Atlas, for in that classic name are implications of its world-wide nature. It might become not only a repository for the latest and best scientific information in all matters relating to land reclamation and afforestation, but demonstrate by practical example how best to reclaim wastelands and deserts. This university should be endowed by all nations, and adequate resources should be placed at its disposal for carrying into effect a large-scale reclamation program which would provide work for 1000 years. Funds commensurate with those at present devoted to armaments should be forthcoming for the gigantic task of reclaiming the waste places of the earth.

As a practical demonstration of what can be done, water might be taken from the Gulf of Gabes and, sweetened by fourteen miles of proper conduits, used to flood an area of three hundred square miles of desert below sea level. This would provide an inland sea and transport for the flourishing areas which would spring up in its neighborhood as a result of bio-technical methods. The rivers flowing south and north from the Atlas, Aures, and Tebessa Mountains might be manipulated to provide power and fertility. This center would become a starting point for a wider reclamation program, which would in time embrace the whole of the Sahara and the Libyan Deserts.

We advocate that all standing armies everywhere be used for the work of essential reafforestation, in the first instance, in the countries to which they belong, and that each country, as it is able to spare men, shall provide expeditionary forces to co-operate in the greater tasks of land reclamation in the Sahara and other deserts. Armies are risky factors in countries where the people cannot be fed, and they will not provide security unless essential food is forthcoming generally. I am confident that all this can be done. The world is technically so far advanced that it is not in a position to stand the privation of descent into chaos and extinction. Under the palpable danger of approaching ruin, it is possible for the best and highest to exercise their authority and turn man from racial suicide back to the light of reasonable preservation.

Archaeologists have given us the story of the rise and fall of nations. Each in turn reached its peak of prosperity, then vanished. We have learned that civilization is an intermittent and recurrent phenomenon, that it sprouts and flourishes, decays and dies. Each successive civilization had its great year, followed by impotence. Each in turn arrived at the crossroads of time, where it was confronted with the necessity of deciding which way to turn.

The red lights are against us in our reckless career. To continue to rape the earth and fight for dwindling supplies of food and timber spells destruction. The murky rivers, charged with earth from many a mountainside, tell their story and are danger signals. Following upon forest destruction, overstocking, and exhaustive cultivation, erosion is taking place over vast tracts of the earth's surface. Let us remember that the empires of Babylon, Syria, Persia, and Carthage were destroyed by the advance of floods and deserts caused by the increasing clearing of forests for farmland. Can the present reckless race to destruction be checked? Will man agree to conserve and replenish the earth and stem the march of the oncoming deserts? It is not merely a national question, but a world undertaking, in which every nation and every member of the human race must take his share.

World War II cost the nations much material. A further war might cost double the amount and reduce us to dire distress. If we spent as generously on land reclamation and reafforestation, we should immediately remove the specter of world war, safeguard the forests, and ensure the prosperous well-being of mankind for generations to come.

The world task which I have attempted to outline calls for authoritative action from the highest and best, and the country that provides the lead in this fateful hour will rise above political and national rivalries and have the support of Heaven and earth. "For the earth is the Lord's and the fulness thereof." Such work, if done in the spirit of worship, will count as worship. By saving the forests and maintaining the tree cover the sudden decline to which civilizations are prone will be avoided.

Such a lead will command the support of the choice spirits in all lands. In times past it has been said that it is the duty of a man to be prepared to die for his country; today it is the duty of every thinking being to live and to serve not only his own day and generation, but also generations unborn by helping to restore and maintain the green glory of the forests of the earth.

INDEX